Holding the Line

Kenneth Ballantyne

75780 Sapper R Hill Royal Engineers – 1915 - 1919

*Cameras were rare at this time and so these studio portraits were
very important for those left behind.*

Holding the Line

The true story of Rowland Hill, ISM,
Royal Engineers
A Sapper on the Western Front in France and
Belgium during World War One

by

Kenneth Ballantyne

"A good book is the precious life-blood of a master spirit."

John Milton

First Published in Great Britain in 2016
by Laundry Cottage Books
Admaston, Shropshire, England
TF5 0AD

Tel: 01952 – 223931
Email: cenneach@westcoast13.wanadoo.co.uk

ISBN 978-0-9550601-8-2

Proofreading & editing by
Sue Browning Editing and Proofreading

Contents

By the same author & published by Laundry Cottage Books in Great Britain:

Another Dawn Another Dusk
ISBN 978-0-9550601-3-7

All the Things You Are
ISBN 978-0-9550601-4-4

First Wave
ISBN 978-0-9550601-6-8

Holding the Line
ISBN 978-0-9550601-8-2

Through the Gate
ISBN 978-0-9550601-9-0
[due for publication 2017]

The Journey
[Title no longer available]

Other titles published in Great Britain by Laundry Cottage Books:

'J' for Johnnie
John Trotman, DFC & Bar
ISBN 978-0-9550601-7-5

The D-Day Dodger
Albert F Darlington
ISBN 978-0-9550601-2-0

Bibliography

A Nurse at the Front, The First World War Diaries of
Sister Edith Appleton; edited by Ruth Cowen; 2012;
Simon & Schuster

Bradshaw's Descriptive Railway Hand-book; 1863;
Old House Books

British History Online – Much Wenlock [pages 399-447]

Forgotten Voices of the Great War; Max Arthur; 2002;
Ebury Press

Goodbye to All That; Robert Graves; 1929;
Penguin Modern Classics

Harry's War; Harry Stinton; 2008; Conway Books

History of the 1st Canadian Division;
Joanna Legg & Graham Parker

It's Only Me; David Raw; 1988; Frank Peters Publishing Ltd

Living Archive Milton Keynes;
Particular thanks to Mr Roland Doggett

Living in Sin: Cohabiting as Husband and Wife in
Nineteenth-Century England; Ginger Frost,
Manchester University Press, 2008, Reviewed by
Dr Tanya Evans, Macquarie University, Sydney

Meteorological Office Weather Reports

Scapa Flow in World War I and II; Charles Tait

Stretcher Bearer; Charles H Horton, edited by Dale le Vack;
2013;   Lion Books

The British Rum Ration; Nick Johnson

The Forgotten Front; Paul Reed;

The German Spring Offensive of 1918; CN Trueman

The Great Battles of World War 1; Jack Wren; 1971;
Hamlyn

The History of Corn in Canada;
    Seedrock Agriculture Research;
The History of Elgin County; Hugh Joffre Sims
The Rum Ration; Tony Allen
The Somme; AH Farrer-Hockley, 1964; Pan Books
They Fought for the Sky; Quentin Reynolds; 1958;
    Cassell & Co
Tommy 1418.com; Ian Houghton
Vocabulary of Native American Languages: Mohawk
What Tommy Took to War 1914 - 1918; Peter Doyle &
    Chris Foster; 2014; Shire Publications Ltd
Wikipedia, the Free Encyclopaedia
Work of RE in the European War, 1914-19,
    The Signal Service (France); RE Priestley;
    2006 Ed, The Naval & Military Press Ltd

Acknowledgements

I am very grateful to the several people who have helped me with this biography, some of whom are sadly no longer with us. This is a book which has been in my mind to write for many years stretching back to the days when I would sit with Rowland's widow, Violet, and listen to her reminiscing about her early years and then of life with Rowland. She had kept so much of Rowland's; his emigration papers, his letters from Canada, and then later on his letters home from the Front, all of which eventually passed to her granddaughter.

In her later years, Rowland's sister, Nellie Smith, wrote her memoirs describing life in Cressage at the end of the 19th and early 20th centuries. This work has provided a window into a world that is now far beyond living memory and has been an invaluable aid to me in writing the early part of this book.

My thanks are also due to Dr Trevor Hill and his wife Margaret of Cressage, for their very kind and willing help in tracking the Hill family tree. The shared surname is wholly coincidental; they assure me that they are not related to Rowland.

During my research, my wife, Elaine, and I stayed at the Silent Picket, the extraordinary bed and breakfast business owned by John & Jennie Knight at Martinpuich in the Somme region of France. Superlatives could so easily flow in rapid succession about the Silent Picket. John's extensive library of books, great and small, written about the Great War are kindly made available to guests either for research or casual reading. So too is John's own encyclopaedic knowledge of the conflict and the Somme in particular. I am immensely grateful to him for all the help and information which he researched and provided to me about Rowland's brother Herbert, and for kindly taking us to the place where he was mortally wounded.

Whilst we were busily researching, visiting, and exploring the context of this part of the Western Front, day after day, morning and night, Jennie fed us with a gastronomic extravaganza of multi-course menus which throughout the week did not repeat any dish. I have no idea how she managed to do that but I am very glad that she did. Thank you so much, Jennie.

For anyone interested in the Great War and wishing to visit the Somme area, particularly if wishing to trace a relative, there is nowhere to stay that could be more appropriate, comfortable, and welcoming than the Silent Picket. www.silentpicket.com

The Commonwealth War Graves Commission continues its wonderful work to maintain so many cemeteries worldwide and to provide informative and poignant displays at many locations. My thanks are due to the Commission for this work on both a personal and general level, and I am most grateful to it and to the Imperial War Museum for having made public some of the photographs reproduced in this work. Unless otherwise indicated, all other photographs are owned by me or have been made available to me.

My grateful thanks also go to all those people, many anonymous, who have kindly uploaded information to the Internet which, piece by piece, helped to provide background for this book.

I am again indebted to Sue Browning of Sue Browning, Editing and Proofreading for once more kindly correcting my literary waywardness and grammatical inexactitudes, and for guiding the flow of this story through the pitfalls of writing. I also add my apologies to Sue for dabbling with the manuscript after she returned it to me and in so doing take full responsibility for any consequential errors.

To say thank you to Elaine for all her support, encouragement and help during the two years that this book has taken to write, seems so inadequate. Without that support during the creation of yet another manuscript, it would not have been completed.

Foreword

"On the north the view was bounded by the long chalk ridge of the Hog's Back, from behind whose eastern extremity rose the towers of the seven skyscrapers which constituted Guildford."
Brave New World – Aldous Huxley [1932]

Nothing was ever quite the same after the Great War. Most of the crowned heads of Europe had lost their thrones. Those who survived did so in a world that was fundamentally changing around them. The terminal decline of the great country estates gathered apace. A combination of crippling death duties and, in too many cases, the son and heir left to lie beneath French or Belgian soil, conspired to hasten that decline. Whilst some welcomed this development, for those whose livelihoods and homes depended upon these wealthy land-owning families, the dismantling of the settled order too often led to unemployment and homelessness. The village entity, which for centuries had nurtured, clothed, and supported a complex weave of interdependent layers of society, began to unravel, beginning the slow decline into a soulless dormitory, stripped of all character, its rich and colourful history reduced to a collection of sepia photographs in an antique shop.

Some of those who had been employed in the big houses and upon the estates before the war had left willingly to fight, others to work in factories. Not all wanted to return to their previous positions, even though they had survived the war largely unscathed. But some knew no other way of life and were too old to change; their future did not lie in the brave new world.

The immense social changes which began after the Great War and assumed a greater urgency after the next one, created Britain's enviable Welfare State, the jewel of which is the National Health

Service. Beyond that, whether such huge social upheaval has merely replaced a very rich but generally philanthropic land-owning aristocracy with a very rich but generally vulgar and not particularly philanthropic land-owning nouveau riche, whilst still leaving the vast majority of the population just as poor relative to disposable wealth, is an interesting point but outwith the purpose of this book. I mention it only because it forms the backdrop to the story.

Born in 1892, the fourth of eight children brought up in the humble surroundings of an agricultural labourer's agrestic cottage, Rowland Hill resolutely followed his ambition for a life very different to the one he had been born into. Determined to break the yolk of nineteenth century peasantry and poverty, he emigrated to Canada in February 1912 fired with ambition, hope, and the optimism of youth. The Great War got in the way of all that he had hoped for in the New World and he returned to England in the autumn of 1914. As a Royal Engineer sapper, he was thrust into the front line trenches where he endured artillery shells, machine guns, snipers, mud, lice, rats, flies, rain, ice, snow and oppressive heat to keep the telephone lines intact and the vital communications flowing.

From the last years of Queen Victoria's British Empire to the first years of Queen Elizabeth's Commonwealth, *Holding the Line* is the true story of one man's experiences living through two world wars and the fundamental social and economic changes which they wrought. The book is not, and does not purport to be, either an academic study of the Great War or a reference work. It is the story of a one man's passage through life; a life, the course of which was fundamentally changed both by the event of the Great War and his experiences during it.

Without losing any of the intimacy of the story, I have tried to weave a wider commentary of the war into Rowland's own startling, sobering, terrifying, pitiful, and sometimes funnily uplifting experiences in the British First Army's occupation of the trenches of northern France and their surrounds on what became known as 'the Forgotten Front'. My intention was to provide a rather different account of the Great War through the eyes of a man who endured almost everything which life in the trenches came to represent, and who almost paid the ultimate price.

In writing this story, I have been very fortunate to have had access to much of Rowland's biographical records from a number of sources. His widow, whom I knew very well for many years before her death and who related so many stories and facts to me, kept much primary source material including letters and documents. His granddaughter, who now holds that material, his sister's memoirs and his military service record have all played an important part in piecing together a picture of the man whose delightful and encouraging story this is.

Kenneth Ballantyne
Laundry Cottage
8th May 2016

Dedication

To the eternal memory of

291799 Signaller Herbert Hill
15th Battalion Welch Regiment

12194 Private George Ballantyne
2nd Battalion Highland Light Infantry

And to each and every other person who gave their lives on land, at sea, and in the air during this 'war to end war'.

"We are as much alive as we keep the earth alive."

"The beauty of the trees, the softness of the air,
The fragrance of the grass speaks to me.
And my heart soars."

Chief Dan George
[born] Geswanouth Slahoot
Chief of the Tsleil-Waututh Nation

Holding the Line

Chapter One

" The fox knew well as he ran the dark,
That the headlong hounds were past their mark;
They had missed his swerve and had overrun,
But their devilish play was not yet done."
From Reynard the Fox – John Masefield

A burnished copper sunset that was the western sky slowly faded behind distant purple hills. The still September air hung in a breathless veil, its cool lingering with the last warmth of the day. With soundless stealth, willows of mist materialised, the ghosts of ages past, floating fingers of gossamer across the meadows reaching out to the haunts of another time. The brown Shropshire cattle, now rarely seen, lay scattered upon the grass quietly ruminating to the ageless rhythm of this tranquil scene, one of which they were so much a part. Little could these gentle creatures know that they were soon to be the silent, unwitting witnesses to the passing of this way of life, that an approaching, as yet unseen, cataclysm would sweep them and so much more aside forever. The new century had dawned in January and for now remained the same as the old one, but the seeds of Armageddon were already being sown and two generations would taste their bitter fruit.

The damp grass beneath my boots felt soft and giving as, following my father, I surreptitiously slipped between the cattle and across the pasture to the brook beyond; the brook that held the trout I hoped to tickle. Tickling trout is an old country trick of catching the fish with bare hands; but, no matter how romantic a notion that might be, it was, and still is, poaching, a fact my father was acutely aware of and had impressed upon me from an early age.

However, my father was also a farm worker and the local rabbit catcher and so had good reason to be on the land. I had not long turned eight years old and was still learning the art. When we arrived at the brook, certain that no-one was around, in particular the gamekeeper, I removed my boots, rolled up my trouser legs and carefully stepped into the cold clear water near to the bank. I knelt down and began to feel under the overhanging rocks with both hands. With a surge of excitement, I felt the smooth skin of the fish near to its tail. Keeping my fingers relaxed but pointing up, I gently caressed its underside until I reached the head. Then I thrust my fingers into its gills whilst grasping the tail end at the same time. But my timing wasn't quite right and, with a flash of silver, away the trout sped, rudely awakened from the trance I had so carefully induced it into.

My father chuckled quietly to himself; time to move on. Replacing my boots and rolling down my trousers to cover my wet legs, disappointedly I trudged after him as we started the business of securing a rabbit for tomorrow's supper. There would be other days and other trout. We all learned how to tickle the trout which, along with rabbit, formed an important part of our diet.

The area that is now Shropshire, England's largest inland county, was completely uninhabited by humans until the Iron Age. Around 500 BC, people began to move into the dense forests of oak, ash, alder, willow, black poplar, beech and other native species which covered the whole north midland plain. However, these peoples were largely hunter-gatherers and used the forests for the bounty of the animals and fruits that they offered. Around AD 58, the Roman fort at Viroconium [Wroxeter] was home to the XIV Gemina Legion and then the XX Valeria Victrix Legion. When the military moved to Chester and left Viroconium to the civilian population, it was the fourth largest Roman town in Britain and its substantial ruins are still there for all to see today. It was built just a few miles to the west of Cressage and on the opposite bank of the River Severn, known to the Romans as Sabrina, but it is unlikely that the village of Cressage became established as a permanent settlement until after the Romans had finally left Britain around AD 450. The village probably started as a settlement around the sixth century, during the middle Saxon period of the Dark Ages, within the Long Forest, the immense area of deciduous woodland which filled the lowland areas of what is now central and north Shropshire. However, by the Middle Ages, these forests had been severely denuded to create cultivated land and were further plundered for their oak trees during the English Civil Wars of 1642 to 1651.

The small, but at the time highly influential, market town of Wellington is about ten miles from Cressage, and on 19th September 1642, Charles I addressed his troops there, declaring, "Religio Protestantium, Leges Angliae, Libertas Parliamenti", that is, he would uphold the Protestant religion, the Laws of England and the Liberty of Parliament. This became known as the Wellington Declaration and effectively fired the starting gun for the English Civil Wars.

Listed in the Domesday Book, the village of Cressage, which is now bisected by the busy modern A458 road, stands on the banks of the River Severn between Much Wenlock and Shrewsbury. Its name derives from the old Anglo-Saxon Christesache or Christ's Oak, the name given to an immense oak tree in the village, thought to have grown where the war memorial now stands. St Augustine, the first Archbishop of Canterbury, is reputed to have preached under this great tree in AD 584. However, if he did, it is unlikely that he did so in AD 584 since he did not land in Britain until AD 597. Whether the date has been distorted down the years and he preached in Cressage at some later time is a matter of conjecture, but his legacy remains in the name of the village.

Sadly, the mammoth oak tree which was once part of the Long Forest has gone the way of all living things. Nevertheless, one of its descendants stood just north of the Shrewsbury road until 1814 when it was struck by lightning and burned down. This tree, known as the Lady Oak, measured forty-one feet and seven inches in diameter and after the fire, part of the wood was made into a table which now stands in the porch of the village church, Christ Church. Today, like the phoenix, a healthy offspring has arisen and is growing within the charred shell of the Lady Oak.

Christ Church was built of Grinshill stone in 1841 at a cost of £1,400, and remains the principal place of Christian worship in Cressage today. There was also a Methodist chapel built in 1854, but this is no longer in use as a chapel, having been converted to a dwelling house.

Our home, Jasmine Cottage, was on the edge of the village along Wood Lane. Over the centuries, there have been six cottages in Wood Lane, all known by a name or by that of their present occupants or even of a previous occupant, long since departed. After my Kidderminster-born namesake Rowland Hill promoted the idea of the postage charge on letters being paid by the sender not the recipient in 1837, followed by the introduction of the Penny Black adhesive stamp in 1840, the numbering of properties gathered apace. We were allocated number 4 but no-one really knew where number 4 was, but they all knew where Jasmine Cottage was and who lived there. Interestingly, although Sir Rowland received all the credit and rewards, including his knighthood, for introducing the pre-paid postal service, his scheme was built upon someone else's idea, that of Scot James Chalmers from Arbroath, who designed the first adhesive postal stamp in 1834. He submitted his concept to Parliament in 1837 and on 2nd October 1839 sent the very first envelope carrying an adhesive stamp to Lt-Col Moberly, who was the Secretary to the GPO.

Originally, Jasmine Cottage was a small crofter's home built in 1403, half timbered with wattle and daub walls, a thatched roof and an ancient yew tree in the garden. Nestling in a small hollow, it was an idyllic setting which could have graced the lid of any chocolate box. The large garden, in which my father grew all the fruit and vegetables we ever needed, rose up gently behind and spread out on both sides. The dusty track that led to the wood and gave the lane its name ran past the cottage a few feet from the front door. On the other side of the lane was a narrow meadow along the far side of which flowed Plocks Brook with its generous bounty of fresh trout waiting to be tickled.

My great-grandfather Aaron was a master cobbler and by the time he was at Jasmine Cottage, his reputation had carried far and wide. The ladies and gentlemen of substance at that time would travel considerable distances to have their feet measured and their shoes made by him. On occasions there would even be queues of carriages in Wood Lane awaiting Aaron to come and measure the feet of one or more of the occupants.

Born on 1st April 1821, Aaron entered the world when the future Queen Victoria was only two and her grandfather George III, was King. He grew up in the small Gloucestershire village of Uley, the seventh of eight children born to William Hill and Ann Spratt. In the early years of the nineteenth century, as he learned his trade he travelled from town to town with a small handcart. By 1840 he had arrived in the pretty and prosperous market town of Bridgnorth, where he met Jane Reese, a widow twelve years his senior. Jane, whose parents were from Sheinton, a hamlet about a mile from Cressage, had married William Mason on 3rd November 1835 in Wellington. Not long afterwards, William died, leaving Jane alone. She secured employment in Bridgnorth as a servant in one of the town's large households. It was whilst there that she met Aaron.

Bridgnorth, a major crossing point of the River Severn since the ninth century, incorporates the twin settlements of High Town and Low Town. Living in the shadows of the old castle which was destroyed by Cromwell's troops in 1646, Aaron built up a substantial reputation as a cobbler. He and Jane were married in 1842 at St Mary Magdalene Parish Church, East Castle Street, on 29th December 1842. This relatively new church, incorporating the much older thirteenth-century site, was completed in 1795. It had been designed by Scottish-born engineer and architect Thomas Telford, who eight years earlier had been appointed Shropshire's Surveyor of Public Works. Included amongst his many notable constructions are the Caledonian Canal and the Menai Suspension Bridge, now a Grade I listed building.

Aaron and Jane's first son, George, was born in 1843 and two years later they left Bridgnorth for Cressage, where they joined Jane's parents in Jasmine Cottage. A year after moving to Cressage, their daughter Ellen, my grandmother, was born, and then in 1851, their third child, William, followed. For the time, it was an unusually small family, perhaps because when they were married Jane was already thirty-three. Much later, the cottage was bought by the family and remained in its ownership until sold at auction on 21st June 1973. By pure coincidence, Jane's mother's maiden name was also Hill. Thus, although completely unrelated to each other, the name Hill was carried by both my maternal great-grandmother and my paternal great-grandfather.

What little education Ellen received came from the day school in Cressage. This was the usual form of very elementary education for the poor in Britain at the time and amounted to the basics of the three 'Rs' and some scripture. Sex education was most certainly not included; that was learned by observing nature in the woods and fields of the countryside. The schools were funded by private donations from local wealthy philanthropic benefactors. By the age of ten Ellen no longer attended school. She continued to help with all the work in the cottage and then at eleven was sent to Wellington to live with her aunt and uncle as their domestic help. It was whilst living with them, that on a cold, dark January night at the beginning of 1864, seventeen-year-old Ellen conceived my father. I have never known the true identity of my grandfather, nor the circumstances of his relationship with my grandmother, Ellen. However, it seems likely that the event involved her uncle. He was not her blood relative but related by marriage through her aunt, and I have no idea whether Ellen was a willing or a naive participant in the activities. I like to think the latter.

Nevertheless, once it became clear that she was pregnant, Ellen was dismissed from her aunt's service and returned home to Jasmine Cottage, where my father was born on 20th September. Had Ellen lived in Dorset, her life of hardship, disappointment, poverty and tragedy which followed from that January night could so easily have inspired Thomas Hardy.

As is so often the case, it started well for her. On 5th June the following year, Ellen married a local man, Thomas Brazier, whom she had met soon after my father was born. Thomas had worked on the building of the Severn Valley Railway until it was opened on 31st January 1862 after the completion of the section to Shrewsbury. During the line's construction, as it approached Cressage from Buildwas, the track bed was laid along the old straight Turnpike road close to the River Severn, necessitating the moving of the village roads to Sheinton and Shrewsbury away from the river to their present positions. Even then known as the Severn Valley Railway, the line was part of the West Midlands Railway until it was absorbed into the GWR network the following year.

1863 was also the year that Bradshaw's Descriptive Railway Handbook was published. An indispensable aid and guide for the Victorian railway traveller in Great Britain and Ireland, the book gave a running commentary about all the towns and cities which the then extensive railway network connected. The commentary on the Severn Valley line includes references to Bewdley, Bridgnorth and Much Wenlock, the latter of which my Bradshaw describes as *'A town of some importance'*.

The SVR became an important link for the villagers to places previously beyond their reach and flourished for a hundred years. Until it came, only the wealthy could travel further afield than half a day's walk. The ancient rights of markets were based upon a radius of six and two thirds miles, which was the distance a man could drive his cattle to market, carry out his business and then drive his newly purchased cattle back home again, between sunrise and sunset. Whilst that distance between markets remains today and is often vigorously enforced through the courts, the railway opened up wider markets and opportunities for the people of Cressage. It took milk from the local farms to the growing population of Birmingham and brought in fresh fish from Grimsby and coal from the Shropshire coalfields; the older children were able to attend the schools in Shrewsbury and Ironbridge and the farmers' wives were able to sell their produce in Shrewsbury, Bridgnorth and Wellington.

However, the rise in motor traffic, both cars and commercial vehicles, after the Second World War brought pressure upon the railway and the inevitable closure. The last train from Cressage was on 23rd August 1963. It ran a return service to Bridgnorth. The line remained in operation a little longer whilst the Ironbridge Power Station was being built, but there were no more passenger services.

Like so many rural communities across Britain which lost their railway links during the 1960s, it was not only a sad time but also the removal of an important element of what held the community together. The great irony now is that the railways today are carrying more passengers than they were at their peak in the 1930s and 40s, but only about two fifths of that network remains. As is almost always the case, here today gone tomorrow politicians are the least capable of people to take long-term strategic decisions. Following the closure of so many of our railway lines and stations, successive governments during the 1960s, 70s and 80s allowed the track beds to be ripped up and the land sold and built upon, or at very best returned to the successors of the original owners; thus in most cases, irretrievably lost forever as a railway route.

With the completion of the line in 1862, Thomas Brazier had lost his job but found work not far away in one of Shropshire's many pits. After they were married, Thomas joined Ellen, her parents, her brother William and my father, little Rowland, in Jasmine Cottage. Two years later, their first daughter Emily was born. Shortly afterwards, Thomas got a job in one of the Staffordshire mines at Newcastle-under-Lyme. Together with Ellen and Emily, he moved to Leycett, leaving my father behind in Cressage. I presume that whilst Thomas was content to marry Ellen, he was not prepared to take on another man's illegitimate child.

At Leycett, Thomas and Ellen had two more children, Alfred and Elizabeth. Towards the end of August 1871, at only eight months old, Elizabeth died. Within a fortnight, Ellen was widowed. On 9th September at the age of twenty-five, whilst working down the pit, Thomas was killed in an accident. After his death, Ellen was left with five-year-old Emily and three-year-old Alfred. With no welfare state to support her, Ellen needed a man to provide for her family and so on 30th December 1872 she married another miner, Thomas Phoenix who also lived in Leycett. Some little time later, they moved to Denbighshire. She had five more daughters and another son with Phoenix, but for Ellen the deaths kept mounting up. By 1883, her first three daughters with Thomas Phoenix and their only son had all died as infants and then her precious Emily, now sixteen and wracked with tuberculosis, slipped away in her sleep one night. Of Ellen's ten children, only my father Rowland Hill, Alfred Brazier, Emily Phoenix, who was named after Emily Brazier, and Jane Phoenix, named after Ellen's mother, would survive childhood.

My father never spoke of his feelings at being left with his grandparents Aaron and Jane, although I always had the impression that he was very happy at the cottage. It was the place where he had been born, where he lived his entire life and where finally, he died. I certainly do not judge my grandmother Ellen, as life was very different then and certainly much harsher. I suspect that Thomas Brazier did not take too kindly to young Rowland, which was all rather fortunate for me because had he done so, my father would not have stayed in Jasmine Cottage, would not have met my mother and I would not have been born.

Over many hundreds of years, the attitude to marriage in Britain has been somewhat ambivalent and was no less so in the nineteenth century. Many couples adopted a form of cohabitation which arose from their circumstances, needs and values rather than only after a formal legal and religious ceremony. The reasons were many, varied and often complex. The most usual reason for unmarried cohabitation was the not inconsiderable impediment that one or both already had an existing spouse. At a time when divorce was both difficult and expensive, cohabitation was a pragmatic solution. For others, when the population was far more static than it is today, consanguineous relationships, especially between first cousins, and incestuous relationships, usually between sister and brother, were far from unusual, particularly in deeply rural areas; consequently, marriage was not available to such couples. A third significant group of people, then as now, were simply unconcerned about the institution of marriage as a factor in their relationship.

In this harsher world devoid of today's social safety nets, for many in the population, relationships were formed from the practical expedient of a woman needing a provider and a man needing a homemaker. I am sure that my grandmother Ellen was no exception to this necessity. Church services which joined two people in the eyes of God might well have taken place when children were on their way but such formality would lag behind the couple's own view of their commitment to one another. Into the mix, by 1861, from a total adult population of around twenty million, there were half a million fewer men in England than there were women.

It is not that Victorian England was any more or any less promiscuous than other generations before or since, it is just that, for many working class families, their priorities were elsewhere, leading to more sexually liberated attitudes and conventionally relaxed communities than is often portrayed. The aristocracy married for money, position and power. The middle classes, always the moral conscience of a nation, married for propriety. The working classes married for necessity. But for all that, individual relationships were still what each couple made them.

My father married Mary Salisbury from Pool Mouth near Wrexham, in Cressage church on 7th July 1884; their first child, my sister Jane, named after our great-grandmother, arrived four days later. Mary was already living in the cottage with my father, although it was still my great-grandparents' home, and the imminence of Jane's arrival would have been abundantly evident to all who had gathered together for the joining of this man and this woman; and very nearly this baby too. Even so, the formalisation which my parents undertook was far from universal.

Over the next few years as their children arrived, everyone in the cottage moved up a little to make room or spread out a little as the older ones left home. Like me, all my siblings were born in Jasmine Cottage. I was the fourth of eight children, venturing into the world on 16th August 1892; the following night, the Meteorological Office reported earthquakes. I like to think it was because the gods were celebrating my arrival! Jane had been born on 11th July 1884, followed by Alice on 29th July 1887, William on 22nd February 1889, then me, then Lucy on 1st March 1895, then Herbert on 14th August 1898, Maud on 21st March 1903 and finally the baby of the family, Sarah Ellen, who was always known as Nellie, on New Year's Day 1905. Some twenty-five years later, Nellie's son Graham would be the last of the family to be born in the cottage.

William died in November 1890 and so I have no recollection of him. It was only my parents and great-grandparents who really remembered him; even Jane was too young to remember him properly. As my grandmother Ellen knew only too well, infant mortality was a fact of life in those days; some children survived and others did not. Indeed, it is a testimony to our parents that they raised seven of their eight children.

My childhood was certainly materialistically poor by today's standards, although that is not to say that we were destitute; far from it. We had all that we needed and much of what we wanted so to that extent, we were well-off and perhaps better off than most modern families. The great consumer society had not arrived and so we weren't forever chasing the pot of gold at the end of the rainbow. There were none of the modern trappings which so dominate family expenditure and haemorrhage money and so we didn't miss them. Much more importantly, we had a very happy home as my parents were devoted to each other and to us. When they married, Mother was twenty-four and Father was still nineteen and they had already been together for some time, but their young love for one another stood the test of the years and they both lived well into their seventies.

Great-grandmother Jane, who was very tall and slim with jet-black hair, was highly independent with opinions ahead of her time; a woman not to be trifled with and one who carried a keen sense of right and wrong. One autumn day when the hunt was out, the hounds were in full cry and very close behind a running fox as the terrified creature, gasping for breath and barely able to continue, staggered over Plocks Brook and headed across the meadow towards the hedge opposite our cottage. It was a lovely afternoon, the sun shone brightly on the front of Jasmine Cottage and Jane was, as on most days, in the kitchen baking bread for the family. She had propped open the front door with one of Aaron's old lasts to let the warm rays of sunshine tumble onto the stone flags of the floor. Hearing the racket sent up by the hounds, she knew that the hunt was close by and nearing its end. She stepped back from her oven for a moment and, from the relative darkness of the kitchen, looked out through the open door into the brightness of the sunlit lane in time to witness the scene which unfolded outside.

The old vixen, with tongue hanging long and low from her mouth, was driven on solely by the fear that gripped her heart. She set off across the open meadow towards her trusty hole through the roadside hedge with the cries and howls of the hounds ringing in her ears. They were already crossing the brook barely yards behind her and, with their quarry in sight, were closing at every stride; she must have known that her cause was lost. At the end of her endurance, she could run no further; this time the hounds would have their kill, her long days in the fields and woods around Cressage would shortly be brought to a violent and painful end in the bright and peaceful surroundings she knew so well. In a few moments, too weak to fight back, she would feel their teeth sink deep into her soft flesh and begin to tear her apart in a frenzied primordial orgy of blood. And yet, even in those last gasping seconds when certain death was nipping at her heels, the exhausted animal remained alert and sharp witted. Ahead of her, she saw a faint glimmer of hope, not without its risk, but certainly the slim distant chance of sanctuary and with it, life. With that flicker of hope came the strength for her final effort. She quickened her pace to the roadside, slipped through the hole in the hedge, across the lane, up the step, in through the open door of Jasmine Cottage and stumbled across the floor to collapse amongst the shadows of the cubby hole beneath the stairs.

Jane was equally sleight of foot. As the fox had come in, she shut and locked the door, then ran across the kitchen to do the same at the back. With the cottage now secure, she left the exhausted fox, its rasping breath resonating around the room, and ran upstairs to her bedroom, leaned out of the open window beneath the overhanging thatch and surveyed the mayhem playing out barely seven feet below her. The Master of the Hunt was imperiously rapping on her front door with his riding crop whilst the hounds milled around the small front garden and the lane in confused turmoil. The Master demanded of Jane that she immediately open the door and release the fox to the hounds. Undaunted by their difference in social status, Jane, assisted psychologically by her slightly higher vantage point and now looking down upon the Master, maintained her composure and replied, "The fox has sought the sanctuary of my home and that is what it is going to get."

The Hunt Master was furious and continued with his demands. However, the strong-minded Jane was not afraid to be true to her beliefs and remained equally adamant that the fox would be spared, finally reminding the Master that he and his hounds had no right to be upon her property, that his dogs were making a mess of her garden, and requesting him to leave. Seeing that further argument was not going to secure the release of the fox, he withdrew his hounds and riders with poor grace and much disgruntlement.

Later, with the cloak of dusk hanging at its deepest, just before total darkness covered the battle ground, and with her own chickens safely locked away for the night, Jane opened the front door. The cool of the evening air swept through the kitchen awakening the razor senses of the vixen. She smelled freedom. Now rested, she slowly emerged from the cubby hole and cautiously crept to the open door. There she lingered and carefully smelled the myriad of scents that drifted by, searching for any hint of danger. Satisfied that all was well, she looked back at Jane standing by the range as if to offer her thanks, then silently slipped away into the beckoning darkness, free, safe, alive again.

Today, when hunting with dogs is illegal, it is perhaps difficult to appreciate how courageous Jane's actions were that afternoon. It was not that she was particularly opposed to hunting; it was an integral part of country life at that time. She knew too well that the fox would have taken her own chickens as quick as lightning given half a chance, but it was simply that she viewed it all as a matter of what was right and what was wrong. The hunt had failed to catch the fox in the open fields and woods and, exhausted though it was, it had outwitted them and had sought the refuge of her home. She was not going see it slaughtered in her own kitchen or chased out to certain death in a one-sided affair in the lane. The hounds had missed their chance that day and the fox had taken hers; it was as straightforward as that. However, in her decision to stand up to the Hunt Master, she was aided in the knowledge that her home was not a tied cottage but was rented from the Duke of Cleveland, who held the manorial rights; there would be no recriminations upon her home and family, and her husband, whose work was widely respected and sought after, was self-employed.

Jasmine Cottage with some of the family at the door

My mother and father. The picture was taken around 1920

Chapter Two

" To bend with apples the moss'd cottage-trees,
And fill all fruit with ripeness to the core;
To swell the gourd, and plump the hazel shells
With a sweet kernel; to set budding more,
And still more, later flowers for the bees,
Until they think warm days will never cease,
For summer has o'er brimmed their clammy cells."
To Autumn – John Keats [1819]

Jasmine Cottage remains one of the oldest cottages in Britain today, and although it has had some modern facilities installed such as an inside bathroom, it is largely unchanged and is, unsurprisingly, a listed building. When we were growing up, though, it was simply called home. There were two rooms downstairs; the main room served as the kitchen, dining room and sitting room, the heart and soul of the house, while the smaller one, which was really a curtained-off area from the kitchen, served as a bedroom for my great-grandparents. The large bedroom upstairs was shared by my parents and all the children, although after Aaron and Jane had died in 1895 and 1897 respectively, first my sisters Jane and Alice slept downstairs in the curtained-off area, and then, when they had left home, Herbert and I slept there. Later still, it became the lodger's bedroom.

There was no running water in the cottage but there was a well in the garden and a spring of beautifully cold, clear, sparkling water that gushed out of the hillside opposite, the original water supply which had led to the cottage being built there in the first place. The lavatory was an earth closet in the garden, so night-time visits were avoided at all costs, especially in the biting cold of the winter. The thatched roof provided its own entertainment and habitat for a variety of creatures. Birds would nest if they could, especially the swallows and house martins. Every year, we had bumble bee nests and spiders aplenty. We always knew when it was going to thunder because long before the clouds appeared, the spiders would start to drop out of the thatch onto the floor and our beds. Our mother hated thunderstorms, though, because she worried about the thatch being struck by lightning. She always hoped that it would rain first to soak the thatch before the lightning started.

Growing up in Cressage and living in Wood Lane was as idyllic a childhood as I think it possible to imagine for any boy or girl from a country family at the end of the nineteenth century. We grew almost everything we needed to eat in the large garden without the help of chemicals, just good honest farmyard manure. The vegetables were gathered in season and eaten fresh; it was the same for the fruit, and the excess of both was laid down for the winter months. Honey from our own bees, eggs from our hens, pork in all its various forms from our pig, home-made beer, and wines from elderberries, gooseberries, plums and parsnips, were all in abundance. What we didn't grow, the countryside around us provided; rabbits and pigeons all year round, supplemented with trout and an occasional salmon or pheasant when the gamekeeper wasn't looking. The hedgerows, woods and fields provided an abundance of seasonal delights, blackberries, wild strawberries, damsons, haws, hazelnuts, several different types of mushroom, elderflowers, and then later the berries, a whole host of herbs including nettles, edible plants and fruits. Milk was one of the very few things that we had to buy, but Dad brought it back with him from the farm and Mum made as much butter as we needed.

The seasons follow a distinct palette in the order of blooms; white in winter, yellow in spring, followed by blues and pinks in summer, with reds and gold heralding the autumn. The hillsides, woods, meadows and banks along the brook seemed to be a carpet of one colour after the other from February to October. Pushing their delicate heads through the late snowfall, the snowdrops promised spring. They were followed by rank upon rank of daffodils, as impressive as anything which had inspired

Wordsworth. Next came the primroses, cowslips and buttercups, then the bluebells, honesty, campion, fritillaries, cornflowers, poppies and foxgloves, whilst the hedges were awash with the delicate pinks and creams of dog roses, honeysuckle and cow parsley. Finally, as the days became shorter and the nights colder, the sap in the trees would fall, turning their leaves to a blaze of reds and oranges and gold before drifting gently to the waiting earth beneath, there for the children to run through and kick up that rustling multi-coloured blanket.

Like every country cottager up and down the land at the time, we kept a pig. When the time came in the autumn, it was slaughtered, scalded and then hung from two great hooks on an oak beam in the kitchen to be butchered. The blood was collected in a pot from which Mother made black puddings, the pig's head was made into brawn, and the trotters were cooked and eaten fresh, as were the chitterlings. Other than the meat, the remaining parts of the pig were made into sausages and pork pies. All the joints and hams were cured with common salt, brown sugar and saltpetre and then wrapped in muslin. In the days before refrigerators and freezers, this was the only way to preserve meat for the long hard winter months that lay ahead. There was nothing wasted from a pig, and the old saying that the only part of a pig that you couldn't eat was the squeal is just about true.

My father rented a small field further up the lane and in the early summer he would mow the hay from it to feed our pony, which, together with the trap, was our only form of transport other than Shanks's Pony, meaning to walk. The saying had entered general use in English by 1785 and probably arose from shank, an old name for the shin bone. After Shank's Pony, most notable connections with the term shank include lamb shank and the nick-name of Long Shanks, given to Edward I who was particularly tall for a thirteenth century man.

Hay making was done by hand with a long scythe. Our faithful dog Tick would sit and watch dad at work, guarding his coat. Presently she would lie down, her eyes becoming drowsy. Finally, sure that they were there for the afternoon, she would let out a long sigh, close her eyes and sleep. In the shimmering heat of those June days, the bronchial five bar burr of wood pigeons calling in the trees, the regular swish of dad's scythe through the grass stems and the whisper of falling swathes were the only sounds to fill the air. The countryside was very often so peacefully and serenely quiet, even in the daytime. The almost constant background cacophony to modern life of aircraft engines, traffic noise, industrial activity, mobile telephones and the irritating, ineluctable 4/4 bass from motor car boom box 'music' systems was completely unknown when I was growing up. Instead, it was nature alone which provided the soundtrack to our days. The unmistakeable call of that harbinger of springtime, the cuckoo, would echo through the woods until he found a mate. In the early summer evenings, the rich melody of nightingales filled the air and lifted even the saddest heart as they called to one another from the secret depths of Wood Lane's thickets. Sadly, the once common sound of this delightful and shy bird is now extremely rare in Shropshire. In wintertime, it could be so quiet that the soft sigh of snowflakes gently falling upon the earth could be distinctly heard; snow on snow, as in that bleak midwinter. For most of Britain, it is impossible to imagine such an intensity of stillness and silence now.

By contrast, at the start of each day, when the first tentative strokes of light touched the eastern sky, the dawn chorus burst upon us with such an intensity of volume that it made further sleep impossible and heralded the beginning of our working day too. The hedgerows, trees and fields were full of birds of every shape and size all singing their greeting to the new day. Lamentably, the dawn chorus has been reduced to little more than a small combo, albeit that they play with equal gusto.

There were no lorries and the sight of a car was so rare that it was quite a spectacle in the village should some intrepid adventurer reach Cressage. Consequently, the air we breathed was much cleaner, although the same could not be said for the larger towns and cities, where heavy industry belched out its putrid and toxic wastes from a forest of towering chimneys. Summer and winter, when not at school or doing our chores in the cottage, we played in the woods, the fields, the brook and the waterfall. We were given our childhood, short though it was, and allowed to be children. We made our own discoveries of the world around us in our own time and nobody ever questioned our safety. We walked wherever we needed to go, to school, to church, to meet our friends, to Cound or to Much Wenlock four miles away on the other side of the now world-famous Wenlock Edge. Dad's pony and trap was for Mother to ride in, not for children.

I do not recall my childhood through rose-tinted glasses because there is no doubt that life for our family, and many others like us, was hard. Our whole domestic world in Jasmine Cottage revolved around the kitchen and the range in particular. The range provided heat for cooking, for water, for warmth; it was the heartbeat of the home and the family. It ran on wood, which had to be sawn by hand, and coal when we could afford it. Out of simple necessity rather than any prudish tilt at decency, we bathed in shifts on Fridays and Saturdays in a tin bath in front of the range fire. The first one in had clean water but less of it, the last one in had mucky water but more of it as little by little it was heated over the fire and poured into the bath. My mother was first in, and then, in order of descending age, my sisters followed her. They bathed on one night whilst my dad, again first in followed by me and then Herbert, on the other night. When Mother and my sisters were bathing, Herbert and I were sent out or upstairs; they always took a lot longer in the bath than we did.

Electricity, which did not come to the village until 1935, was only missed in retrospect. All the labour-saving devices and luxuries which we take so much for granted today were unknown then, so nobody missed them. Only cities and larger towns were lit by street lights, almost all of which were gas. The vast majority of Britain was lit at night only by the moon and the stars; the concept of light pollution was unknown to us. On a moonless night, it was possible to stand outside the cottage door and gaze up to the heavens and see the immense celestial display of stars, which seemed unending, as indeed it was. The pitch-dark sky was filled with countless tiny pinpoints of sparkling light, so many that for people used to walking in the dark they seemed to light the way home.

Inside, our homes were lit by candles and oil lamps, both of which cost money, so for poorer families with little by way of disposable income, getting up and going to bed was closely aligned with the hours of natural daylight. Mains water and drainage, which came to Cressage as late as 1964, was perhaps the greatest social advance for the village in terms of both labour and health; until then, water for our homes came from wells and springs.

May was always a busy month but such a lovely one, and it is not difficult to see why May Day was so important to country communities. The festival dates back to pagan times across the northern hemisphere. It has been celebrated by all cultures for thousands of years and is traditionally the first day of summer. The winter is well and truly past, the sun has real warmth in it, the trees and hedgerows bloom and blossom; a time of plenty is coming again after the lean, dark days of the winter. In these early years of the twentieth century, country life, especially for land workers, still revolved around the seasons, the weather and daylight. Other than when at school, few children spent any time inside unless they were ill or the weather was just too bad to go out; cold weather did not stop us, only incessant rain or storms, of which there were plenty enough over the years.

I don't remember it ever raining on May Day, though perhaps it did. We had a maypole in the school yard around which the girls and the younger boys would dance in and out of each other, weaving the brightly coloured ribbons into the intricate pattern of the pole. Later in the month, from 1904 onwards, the village, along with the rest of Britain, celebrated Empire Day on 24th May each year, or the day before if the 24th was a Sunday, with great enthusiasm. The celebration was started in Canadian schools at Dundas, Ontario, in 1898 by Clementina Trenholme and introduced to Britain in 1904 by Lord Meath. The 24th May was chosen as this was Queen Victoria's birthday. In 1958, post-colonial Britain renamed it Commonwealth Day. In 1976 it was moved to the second Monday in March to divorce it from the historical connection with Queen Victoria and Britain's imperial past. However, with the move to March, the day is no longer celebrated as a public holiday, which was no doubt the intention of the 1976 government.

Lady Elizabeth Harnage, the widow of Sir Henry Harnage and who lived in the village, was a great royalist and supporter of Empire Day, and all the seventy or so children from the school would gather in the school yard to wait for her Ladyship to arrive. Just before she did so, my father would scale the tall flagpole there to secure the Union flag. When everyone was ready, the boys with drums and sticks and the girls, each with a small Union flag provided by her Ladyship, would salute the main flag then set off, drums beating and flags waving, to the top of the village by the vicarage, then down to the bottom by the shop, singing the patriotic songs of the day, *Rule Britannia*, *Hearts of Oak* and suchlike. Lady Elizabeth remained at the school, and as we passed her, the boys saluted and the girls curtsied. There was no traffic thundering and speeding through the village then, so the road provided an ideal route. Everyone thought that this was a wonderful event, not least because it gave people a day off work and, most years, the children a day off school too.

The British Empire, albeit short-lived as empires go, was nevertheless the largest and arguably the greatest empire that the world has ever seen. Whilst it is fashionable today to be critical of imperial Britain, when I was growing up we were all immensely proud of what our nation had achieved and what it had given to the world. Moreover, without that empire, it is almost certain that we would have been unable to defeat the Kaiser or, a generation later, Hitler. Had we not done so, the free world would look very different today.

Society was much more courteous then, irrespective of who you were or how wealthy you were. Manners, once learned, applied to all walks of life. A well-mannered man would raise his cap upon greeting any woman or stand aside to allow her to pass through a gateway first. Elizabeth Harnage had taught us that money did not teach manners; it was education which did that. When she had married Sir Henry on 20th September 1866, he had been a very wealthy man and she had enjoyed a most pleasant life at Belswardyne House, her husband's home. However, upon Sir Henry's death in 1888, she found that the house and most of the estate was mortgaged to pay for his gambling debts. She had been left with a small private income and so had moved from the great house to Littlecote. The house was actually two fine old, modest properties on Sheinton Road close to the crossroads in the village, which she had put together to make one. With her, she had taken her housekeeper and two maids. Nevertheless, far from being bitter about her reduced circumstances, she continued to devote much of her time and energies to helping the villagers, and in particular she tried to help the boys get a good start in life.

Elizabeth was the daughter of Edward Egremont, vicar of Wroxeter and, in keeping with her Victorian upbringing in such a home, she held Bible classes in her house every Sunday afternoon to which almost all the young children in Cressage went. Although we knew her as a comparatively elderly lady, she was always kind hearted, cheerful and interesting. She had no children of her own and I think that is why she enjoyed having us all in her house. Together with my younger brother Herbert, William and George Griffiths and Edward Mullard, I attended these classes because of the wider knowledge which we gained there. William went on to have a good job with the General Post Office before going out to Africa. George made a successful career in the Royal Navy, rising to quite a high rank, Ed Mullard also did well with the GPO, and this lady bountiful would shape my own future too one day in ways that I could not have imagined at the time.

Even after her death on 9th October 1918, she continued to help the poorest and most needy in the village. Her Will contained a charitable legacy, the Charity of Dame Elizabeth Sara Maude Harnage, *'for the relief of persons resident in the Parish of Cressage who are in condition of need, hardship or distress either in gifts of kind or grants of money.....'*. Whilst the villagers all respected her position, we were also genuinely very fond of her as a person, and she was greatly missed.

Building upon a 1643 decision of his father, Charles II created the General Post Office in 1660 as a department of state to carry royal and government documents, but with the introduction of the Penny Black and pre-paid postage, the Royal Mail letter business grew rapidly. The nineteenth and early twentieth centuries saw the development of the telegraph, the telephone, the radio and then television, all of which came under the auspices of the GPO, which by then had become a major employer in Britain. In 1969 the GPO as a department of state ceased to exist, its assets being transferred to the Post Office, which became a statutory corporation and which, in turn, was split up and partly privatised in the 1980s. However, long before such changes were wrought upon it, I too would work for the GPO. The radio, so much a part of people's lives for over a hundred years, was originally known as the wireless. Over time, the name was considered old fashioned and was dropped in favour of the more modern American description, the radio; today, wireless is once more the in-vogue description given to cutting-edge telegraphic communication. There is not much in this world which is truly new; what goes round does indeed come round.

There were two classes in the village school, one for infants and the other, taught by the headmaster, for the older children up to the age of twelve, when compulsory schooling ended. Indeed, it was not until the 1870 Elementary Education Act that compulsory education for five- to ten-year-olds was introduced, and even then, there was a local discretion in rural areas to reduce the upper age. Economic necessity usually required country children to leave school as early as possible to work on the land and obtain paid employment to help the family. Agricultural wages were always low; sometimes they were not as low as at others, but always low. With the coming of the Industrial Revolution, the incomes for farm workers lagged far behind their equivalents in the towns and cities, causing an inevitable labour shortage in the country as people drifted to the conurbations in search of those higher-paid jobs. The shortage was always felt the most during the sowing and harvesting seasons.

I enjoyed my years at school and had always done well there. My father could turn his hand to anything and was very practically minded. I had inherited these skills, but I had also inherited my mother's liking for reading and writing. In 1904, the Shropshire Branch of The Royal Society for the Prevention of Cruelty to Animals, which was founded in 1824 and of which King Edward VII and Queen Alexandra were the patrons, ran an essay-writing competition amongst all the schools in the county. One bright sunny day in June that summer, the headmaster gathered all the children together in the school yard and then called for me to come forward. I could not imagine what terrible transgression I had committed that warranted the presence of the whole school at my admonishment.

My fears were short-lived. As I approached the headmaster, he beamed at me with an expansive smile and announced that he was immensely proud that a pupil of his school had been awarded the county's first prize in the RSPCA essay competition for my story about the care of animals, something which my parents had always instilled in me. They taught me that we must always remember domestic animals should be well looked after and treated with kindness during their lives and that wild animals sometimes needed our help too, even if only to put out water when the brook was frozen over. I had included the story of my great-grandmother Jane and the fox in my essay, which may have resonated with the assessors.

Whether it did or not, I too was very proud of my achievement as I knew that there would have been better-educated children from more affluent backgrounds elsewhere in Shropshire who would also have been able to write very good essays. My prize was a large hard-backed, linen-bound volume of their book, *Animal World*, which I still have today. It was the most memorable occasion of my formal schooling. 1904 was undoubtedly a very good year for me at school because, in addition to the RSPCA prize, I also passed my Religious Knowledge examination with a Credit, and was given an illuminated certificate by John Ramsay Pyle, the Diocesan Inspector. My mother was very proud of me as she was a member of the church choir and involved with all sorts of church activities.

Inevitably for a family living deep in the country at this time, animals, whether wild or domestic, were an integral part of our lives. Of them, however, the foxes were undoubtedly the most enigmatic; both a constant joy and a constant hazard. They are wild animals and have to live just as we do, but they have no shops to go to for their food, so they take it where they find it. Much maligned and persecuted, I do not believe that they deserve their reputation. Certainly there are many cases where a fox has got into a chicken coop and in a frenzy has killed all the chickens, but without human intervention, the chickens would not have been closed up and unable to escape, so it wouldn't happen in the natural wild. We are hardly in a position to accuse the fox, for of all the animals that inhabit this earth, there is none that knows more about needless killing than mankind, as I was to find out all too soon.

Foxes are fascinating creatures and every bit as capable of having fun as we are. More than once I have seen a fox playing with one of our dogs, chasing around a field and rolling over with each other for nothing more than the sheer exhilarating indulgent pleasure of doing so. They are also highly intelligent and superbly adapted to their environment. I have seen a fox that, when being chased by the hounds, has jumped onto a sheep's back, making it flee in panic across the field, only for the fox to jump off again on the other side. The pursuing hounds were left to mill around the field in disarray and dismay at the sudden loss of scent. Similarly, I have been there when, with equal effectiveness, the fox has run up a stream or along the top of a drystone wall.

Mankind has consistently shown that he is genetically incapable of taking part in any contest without seeking to gain some sort of subversive advantage over his opponent, be it in sport or in war. Blocking up the entrance to the lair of a fox is the admission of human failure at all levels bar the lowest. Mostly, the foxes that are caught by the hunt are the old and the infirm; a young healthy fox is far too smart for the hounds.

One day, Dad came home with a small fox cub whose mother had been killed. He made a pen for the cub and we nurtured it for several weeks, each day running around the garden with it and brushing its beautiful reddy-brown coat until it shone. It was Father's intention to take the fox deep into the woods and return it to the wild, but one night shortly before he was able to do so, the fox escaped. With the call of the wild beating strongly inside its breast, the pull was too great; he broke out of the pen and slipped away. Next day, we searched for several hours until, at last, late in the day, there he was, under the hedge up at the allotments along Wood Lane; shot by a local farmer.

Harvest was always the busiest time of the year and all the children helped to gather it in. It didn't matter how young or old you were, there was always a job to do at harvest, and few children, especially the boys, spent any time in school when it was under way, hence the long summer holiday. As children, we would follow the reaper-binder and gather up the sheaves of oats or wheat or barley and stand them in stooks to allow the air to dry them. Then, after a few days, they would all be gathered in. The men would throw them up onto the carts and off they would go to the farms for threshing to separate the grain from the straw, which was then made into ricks before being used for winter bedding or feed for the cattle.

One of the main jobs in the fields for the young children when the harvest was being gathered in was to chase the rabbits out from under the stooks where they hid when anyone was about. Once out in the open, they were caught by the dogs or shot by the men and would end up in a pie or a stew at home; either way, they were destined for the pot. After all this work, Harvest Festival was a real celebration and people enjoyed themselves, especially if it had been a good harvest safely gathered in.

Before the days of television and cars, when most country roads were not yet metalled, rural communities were quite isolated. At the end of the nineteenth century, the main form of transport for any distance was the railway, and so communities made their own entertainment and Cressage was no exception. We were very lucky in the village as there were several talented musicians and singers, all of whom would happily perform on a regular basis.

Sisters Gertrude and Ethel Jones organised all sorts of concerts with glittering costumes for the girls to wear. Like our parents, my sisters and I sang in the church choir; most of the boys and girls of the village were in the choir and attendance at church services was more or less compulsory. It did, though, have its compensations, as during the summer months we had several day trips to the seaside. These were immensely exciting occasions and looked forward to with great anticipation; catching the early train to the Welsh coast and then arriving back home in the late evening, tired but very happy.

The 12th May each year brought the Much Wenlock annual games and fair. In 1850, Dr William Penny Brookes founded the Wenlock Olympian Class, later the Wenlock Olympian Society, and in that year the first modern Olympic Games were held. With a few interruptions along the way, they have continued ever since and are the true home of the modern Olympics. Although the competitors took the games very seriously, for us it was a wonderful day out as there were all sorts of attractions and stalls at the fair as well as the games, including watching the farmers on their great Shire horses thundering across the field and jousting as medieval knights would have done, perhaps on the very same field.

We walked to Wenlock in loose gangs of boys and girls and stayed late into the evening before setting off back. No thought was ever given to catching the train; money was short and a train journey would have cost valuable pennies. We thought nothing of walking the four miles to Wenlock and back again, as we did it quite often. Wenlock was the regional town for us and would supply whatever we needed that wasn't available in Cressage. Trips as far away as Shrewsbury, the county town, Bridgnorth or Ironbridge, just down the valley from Coalbrookdale, the birthplace of the Industrial Revolution, all about twelve miles distant, were very rare before the railway came and many villagers never ventured further than Wenlock throughout their entire lives.

During the golden age of agriculture from 1830–1870, when weather patterns were stable and kind, with few foreign imports of food and advances in machinery and methods, British agriculture enjoyed bountiful years of which 1863 was probably the best. In these years, farm workers could expect to earn around ten to twelve shillings per week, with extra during the long days of harvest time. However, by the mid 1870s, the weather patterns had changed; the years of regular bountiful harvests were a thing of the past. There had been a series of wet summers producing poor harvests and diseases in both sheep and cattle. To make matters worse, the rest of the world was catching up with our technology.

As the nineteenth century had drawn to a close and the golden years were little more than a pleasant memory, wages had once more fallen far behind those of factory workers, even though farming as an industry produced something around 20% of the nation's wealth at the time. My father worked for Mr John Preece, who farmed at Cressage House, and later on for his son. In the closing years of Queen Victoria's reign and for many years after, Dad was paid just fourteen shillings a week, not much more than he would have earned twenty years earlier, and so his rabbit catching was an essential supplement to our meagre income. By 1906, though, it was widely believed that the worst of the slump in farming was behind us and the future began to look brighter.

Before his retirement in 1913, Dr William Packer was the doctor for all the village families. However, it was his little son Herbert who was destined to become Admiral Sir Herbert Annesley Packer, KCB, CBE, RN, probably the most famous inhabitant Cressage has produced. The only son of the doctor and musician Edith Rutter, he was some two years my junior and, together with his sisters Dorothy, Winifred and Marion, grew up at The Mount in Shore Lane, just over the brook and across the field from Jasmine Cottage. I knew Herbert well in the way that young children within a small village know each other, but of course we were socially separated, and as we grew towards twelve years of age and the start of our working lives, contact inevitably became confined to the civilities of incidental greetings. It seems inconceivable now, but with his parents' blessing and encouragement, Herbert left his home in Cressage at the age of thirteen to join the Royal Navy. In 1907, there was nothing unusual in this. During the Great War, Herbert Packer served in the battleship HMS *Warspite*, where in 1916 as an Acting Sub-Lieutenant Assistant Gunnery Officer at the Battle of Jutland, he was Mentioned in Dispatches.

In 1943, in the midst of the Second World War and now a Royal Navy Captain, Herbert was given the command of his old ship, HMS *Warspite*, aboard which he felt completely at home. Later that year, he was once more Mentioned in Dispatches, achieving the very rare distinction of being twice Mentioned whilst serving in the same ship in two different wars twenty-seven years apart. 1943 also saw his promotion to Rear Admiral, whereupon he was appointed to the highly important position of Chief of Staff. In 1950 he was promoted to Admiral and knighted. He died at his home called Cressage in South Africa in September 1962 aged 68.

The modern perception is that children grow up much more quickly today than they used to; I don't think so. We left school at thirteen, before if possible, and went straight into work. Herbert Packer, like many others, had left home for a life in the Royal Navy; he hadn't run away to sea but was following the recognised structured career passage for the Service. I would be surprised if there were many thirteen-year-olds able to cope with that now.

Chapter Three

"I am going to pack my two shirts with my other socks and my best suit in the little blue cloth my mother used to tie round her hair when she did the house, and I am going from the valley"
How Green Was My Valley – Richard Llewellyn

By the time I reached my thirteenth birthday in August 1905, I had already started a full-time job as a farm worker. My older sisters, Jane who was by then twenty and Alice who was seventeen, had both long since left home and gone into domestic service, which in their cases had started when they were only twelve. There was always plenty of work for domestic servants. In addition to the grand houses of the very rich, most middle-class families employed maids; even the most modest-income families had at least one maid. Consequently, since women generally did not work after they were married, there was always plenty of demand for girls and young women to enter domestic service straight from school or soon after, and because they would usually live in, their accommodation costs were reflected in the low wages that were actually paid to them.

Elizabeth Harnage taught me the joy to be had from reading. There was no spare money in our home to buy books, but Lady Harnage had a wonderful library suitable for all ages and would happily allow anyone to come to her house and read. I passed many Sunday afternoons reading the likes of RM Ballantyne's *Coral Island*, *The Young Fur Traders*, *The Dog Crusoe* and *Ungava: a Tale of Eskimo Land*. It was these last three which first awakened my interest in Canada, a country in which, from the age of sixteen, Ballantyne had spent five years working for the Hudson's Bay Company, trading with the local indigenous peoples. The stories in his books which were aimed at a young readership were based upon his own experiences whilst in Canada. Later, I read other classic novels such as Herman Melville's *Moby Dick* and Mark

Twain's adventures of Tom Sawyer and his friend Huckleberry Finn along the Mississippi river. Increasingly, all this was something that I too wanted to experience.

I loved the Shropshire countryside but, perhaps from my reading, I was restless for something else, though didn't know what. For now, though, there was work on the farms even for a thirteen-year-old lad. Long before my last day at school, I had secured a job with Mr Preece on the same farm as my dad. Although still growing, I was already quite a strong, stocky lad, and as I had helped out on the farm in my holidays for several years and especially with the harvest, he was happy to take me on. It was important for me to have got a job before the days began to grow shorter with the onset of the autumn, because there was generally less to do around the farm in winter and casual or seasonal labour was always shed at that time.

My eight years at the village school had equipped me well for the world in which I was growing up. I had excelled in the three 'Rs'; reading writing and 'rithmetic. I had already demonstrated that I could read and write to an accomplished level and I had a good grasp of fundamental arithmetic. But the school had taught us all much more than that. We had learned about our history, studied geography enough to know where we were in the world and the bounds of the British Empire upon which the sun never set. The senior classroom wall was adorned by a large map of the world upon which all the countries that made up that Empire were coloured in red. It spread around the globe and amounted to about one quarter of the land mass and was an impressive achievement for such a relatively small country.

The one country, however, which increasingly fascinated me was Canada. I think it was the seemingly boundless immensity of it all that gripped me. The vast forests that grew over hundreds of miles without a break and the animals that lived in them; the Great Lakes, so large they created their own weather systems and froze so hard in the winter that they became byways for the trackers; stories about the peoples of the First Nations who not so very long ago had been the only humans in that wilderness; the prairies of the south-west that stretched further than the eye could see and took days on a train to cross. The more I read about Canada, the more it gripped me and the less content I became at the prospect of spending the rest of my life in Cressage.

Northern Europeans had been emigrating to Canada for several decades, drawn by the prospect of certain work and, above all, opportunity. I talked to my dad about my dreams of going to Canada and, far from dismissing my ideas, he encouraged me. However, he did give me the one piece of valuable advice which would shape my future; that I should try to learn a trade before I was much older so that I did not spend the rest of my life grafting on the land as he had done.

In a relatively short period of time, Alexander Graham Bell's invention of the telephone changed the world. The ability to talk to other people who were many miles away quickly captured the imagination of those who could afford to have it installed. Middle-class women in particular enjoyed the opportunities it offered them to keep in contact with friends whilst their husbands were at work. It was an important factor in breaking down the isolation which many women experienced and also provided employment opportunities for single women who worked as telephonists in the exchanges. The lines suspended upon the telegraph poles with white china insulators were gradually advancing across the countryside, linking cities, towns and villages. By the 1930s they had become an integral and ubiquitous sight at the side of roads and railway tracks up and down the country. Small local switchboards as well as the large city boards were staffed almost exclusively by women telephonists, who would sit in front of the equipment to push in and pull out the bayonet plugs for each line as they connected callers one to another.

Through the ears of the telephonist, the village switchboard became the fountain of all gossip and other useful local information. Once having connected the caller to the recipient, if the telephonist did not flick the semaphore switch on the board beneath that particular line, then she could hear both sides of the conversation through her headset. All strictly against the GPO rules, of course, but so often not to do so was simply a temptation too far, especially for the more interesting or salacious conversations. Such eavesdropping was a fact of village and small-town life which crime writers such as Agatha Christie would come to embrace as an essential ingredient of many a plot. By 1910, I had become fascinated by the working of the telephone, even though we could never have afforded to have one installed, and I read everything that I could about how it worked and the lines that carried the impulse signals.

On 6th May that year, sixty-eight-year-old King Edward VII died at Buckingham Palace as a result of several heart attacks, bronchitis and pneumonia. His body lay in state in Westminster Hall from the 17th to 19th May and the funeral which followed was the last great gathering in Britain of royal households. Forty-nine royal heads of state, including nine reigning European kings attended. A further twenty-one royal princes and princesses were joined by political heads of state. All the nine European monarchs were related to Edward and through him to each other either by blood or by marriage. The occasion was later described by Barbara Tuchman in her work *The Guns of August* as, "*the greatest assemblage of royalty and rank ever gathered in one place and, of its kind, the last.*" Indeed, many would not keep their thrones for much longer.

There was no television and few homes had a wireless set, consequently reporting the daily events of the arrangements for the funeral and the assembled noblesse was the province of the newspapers. For Elizabeth Harnage, the great royalist in Cressage, the death of a second monarch within ten years was a terrible occurrence and she religiously followed the unfolding events through the newspapers. When the day came, much of the country stopped. The King's funeral cortège was captured on film by the Pathé News cameras and shown in cinemas over the following few days, without sound, of course.

Although the feudal system of servitude and church tithes had faded away by the early twentieth century, there was still a very rigid structure to society, both here in Britain and across Europe; it was a structure which, with better education and communications, was being questioned and challenged. Social and penal reformists, usually from well-educated middle-class backgrounds, continued to seek improvements in industrial working conditions, housing provision and the treatment of prison inmates.

As Prince of Wales, Edward had enjoyed the excesses of privilege and pleasure, but as King he fulfilled the challenge of his destiny. During his short reign, Edward VII put in place or oversaw the beginnings of some of the most profound and fundamental changes which would affect, and still continue to affect, our lives. He travelled widely in Europe and played an important part in creating the 1904 Entente Cordiale with the French and the Triple Entente between Russia, France and Britain, both of which would, ten years later, be pivotal in the political machinations before the outbreak of war and determine upon which side the different countries lined up to fight.

Socialism had become a potent force in Britain; the Labour Party and trades unions increased their influence and power. The 1906 and 1911 Liberal governments initiated many social reforms which are recognisable today in our modern welfare state. Pensions for the elderly, the introduction of labour exchanges, health and unemployment insurance and free school meals were all introduced before 1914, although since free school meals were optional, many local authorities with less forward-thinking and philanthropically minded councillors refused to provide them because to do so would bring about a small increase in the domestic rates.

In the late nineteenth century and the first years of the twentieth, the suffragette movement, which had been started by Mary Smith in 1832, gained many more members and much publicity, particularly after Emmeline Pankhurst and two of her daughters formed the Women's Social and Political Union, embarking upon a course of positive action which often brought them into conflict with the law. There were other suffragette groups which had different approaches and did not engage in criminal activity, but all sought not only votes for women but also greater emancipation and career opportunities. Better education meant that children from poorer families left school later and were more accomplished at reading and writing than their parents. Revolution was in the air across Europe, and whilst it was probably less imminent in Britain than was feared at the time, there were many thousands of people who felt the same way that I did and wanted something better than simply doing what generations before them had done.

In June 1910, Liverpool hosted the Royal Agricultural Show for the third time. Several of the Cressage farmers, including Mr Preece, went to the Royal Show each year, and this year for the first time he took my dad, who was the head dairyman on the farm, with him. When Dad got home, he told me all about the new machinery on display, including the latest 'Alfa-Laval' cream separator, which took first prize and the gold medal in the trials organised by the Royal Agricultural Society. In the world of cream separators, no other manufacturer could come close to Alfa-Laval, and for years there were more of their separators sold to farmers than all the other makes put together. He told me of all the fine horses, cattle, sheep, pigs, poultry and other animals to be seen at the show, and then he gave me a little memento of his day there. Whilst visiting the stand of J Bibby & Sons, the compound animal feeds producers whose head offices were next to the docks, he was given a complimentary pencil. It was a beautifully made small flat designed pencil encased in a pewter holder about the size and shape of a pocket penknife. The outside of the case said, 'Souvenir of the Royal Show Liverpool 1910 with compliments of J Bibby & Sons, King Edward Street, Liverpool'. It was intended for use around the dairy but I kept it safe and took it with me to Canada, France and Belgium. Like my school prize, I still have it to this day.

The year ended wet and warm. The rain seemed incessant, and at Cressage, the Severn burst its banks early in the month, flooding all the water meadows on both sides. When the year turned, most of these fields were still flooded. Working out on the land, the unseasonably warm weather was not altogether unwelcome despite the rain, although there was some concern that the newly ploughed fields were not getting the frost that they needed to break down the soil and kill off any lingering pests. If the cold weather didn't come soon, it could mean problems for the following year's crop. But Jack Frost was in no rush to arrive and December 1910 passed without ice or snow. It was the warmest December ever recorded in England and it would remain so for another 105 years.

By now I was eighteen and everyone in the village knew that I wanted to emigrate to Canada. A year after King Edward's funeral, my sister Maud came home with a newspaper cutting for me which she had been given by Lady Harnage. It was an advertisement from the Canadian government offering land and opportunities to British farm workers who wanted to emigrate there. The country was particularly short of farm workers for many of the same reasons that affected British farms. They were so anxious for British workers to emigrate there that amongst other ideas to attract us, they sponsored an essay-writing competition the first prize for which was free passage for the family and a free homestead when they got to Canada. Unfortunately, the competition was only open to school children; it had rather come a little too late for me, although I doubt that my mother and father would have left Cressage for Canada in any event.

Much as had happened in Britain, people were leaving the land to find work in the cities where the wages were higher and the opportunities greater; but I would be happy to go. I was working on a farm here, so I may as well work on one there for a short time because I knew that it would be my way into Canada. The main Canadian Government Emigration Offices had been in Trafalgar House since 1903, but by 1911 the high volume of applications had required additional office space to be taken, so in answer to the advertisement, I wrote to the new office at 11–12 Charing Cross, London, and within a month had received the details of the scheme and an application form.

The form asked for the usual information from applicants, including full name, date of birth, address, nationality, sex, whether married or single, occupation, whether I could read and write, if I had ever been in prison, my state of health, who was to pay my contribution to the fare, how much money I would have with me on arrival and so on. It had to be accompanied by a one-pound deposit, which was about two weeks wages for me, and I was assured that the date and port of departure, port of arrival and place of employment would all be sent to me in due course.

It was what I had been waiting for. I had been saving hard for my passage, even though the sea crossing and train to my destination was to be assisted by the Canadian government, and it had been a long slog to save enough money for my ticket together with some extra to have in my pocket in reserve. From my weekly pay I had to give some to my mother for my keep, buy my own clothes and boots and put a little aside for social activities, but the rest went into my emigration fund; I was determined to seek a better life for myself. My intention was to take advantage of the government

54

scheme to assist immigrants to become landholders, but if all else failed, I had resolved to seek work as a telephone lineman, the opportunities for which seemed much greater there.

Canada was in dire need of manpower and opportunities there were plentiful. The government's promise of 160 acres of prairie land given for the price of a $10 registration fee after two years' work was very attractive; it was so much more than I could ever have achieved here. All across northern Europe, the population was growing rapidly, the old social structures were breaking down and people were moving from the land to the industrial cities. At the same time, Canada found itself, partly by chance and partly by design, in the right place at the right time to receive these émigrés.

In 1885, the Canadian Pacific Railway had been completed, so linking the east and west coasts with each other and with the interior. Then, on 16th August 1896, which coincidentally had been my fourth birthday, George Carmack and his First Nation brother-in-law Skookum Jim discovered gold in Rabbit Creek, a tributary of the Klondike River in the Canadian Yukon; the gold rush followed and brought 100,000 prospectors pouring into the area. The easy gold quickly ran out and then more was found in Alaska, but by 1899, it was all over; the losers were the indigenous peoples of the area, the nomadic Hän tribe.

The prairie grasslands of south-western Canada had generally been considered to be too dry to produce wheat in significant amounts. But in 1903, a new strain of wheat was developed that was suitable to be grown in this semi-arid region, which borders with the United States along the 49th parallel, and by 1911 it was being grown commercially in substantial quantities. New grain mills grew up needing manpower. Finally, all this coincided with the closing of the United States borders with Canada, stemming the flow of Americans looking for work and that is why Canadian farmers were desperate for farm workers.

August 1911 saw my nineteenth birthday arrive, but since it fell on a weekday, it was work as usual. However, my mother had baked a wonderful fresh plum cake for me, and Herbert, Lucy, Nellie and George Aston, our lodger, didn't need asking twice to help me eat it that evening. After Jane, Alice and Maud had all left home to go into service, Father took in George as a lodger. George's rent to my mother helped towards the family finances since Herbert and the girls were still at school.

Jane had been stepping out with Edwin Higginson from the village for some time and in November they were married at Cressage church. Typical for November, the weather was dull, damp and dour but we had a good family gathering at the cottage as they started what would be almost sixty years together.

Towards the end of the year, I received a reply from the Emigration Offices; my application had been accepted and I was on my way to the New World and a new life. My destination in Canada was to be Aylmer in Ontario province. All the family were very supportive of my adventure, but inevitably, as the departure date drew nearer, we became more aware of the implications. I was not just going to leave home, that was expected, but at a time when most people did not travel very far, I was going to leave England and would probably never see any of them ever again. Lucy had left to go into service, so after I had gone, it would just leave Herbert, Maud and Nellie at home; we tried to make the Christmas of 1911 even more special than it had always been.

When New Year's Day 1912 dawned, it brought in the third leap year of the twentieth century and my sister Nellie's seventh birthday. The day also saw the birth of Kim Philby, who would grow up to become the infamous senior British Intelligence officer who spied for the Russians and became known as 'the Third Man'; Guy Burgess and Donald McLean were the other two in the scandal of the 1950s, which later uncovered Anthony Blunt and possibly John Cairncross, collectively known as 'the Cambridge Five'. The year would also see a number of other memorable events besides my departure to Canada, including Captain Scott's ill-fated expedition to the South Pole.

On 16th April 1912 Harriet Quimby became the first woman to fly across the English Channel, just short of three years after Louis Blériot's historic pioneering flight. The public, though, hardly noticed her achievement; the loss of the *Titanic* a few hours earlier filled the newspapers and her feat was largely unreported. Other notable events that year included the births of Odette Sansom and Nancy Wake, both of whom thirty-three years later would become two of the most remarkable and courageous women agents of the Special Operations Executive, the SOE, to survive the Second World War.

The cold, wet, dark days of January were always a hard slog for anyone who was required to work outside. The ground was either as hard as iron with frost and snow or else a quagmire of mud from endless rain. In January 1912 it was the quagmire. My boots were wet and never dried out. Each evening I scraped away the mud that caked them, knowing that the next day they would be covered again within minutes. I thought that the mud of that wet miserable winter was bad enough but I had no idea just how deep and appalling mud could be; how much it would come to haunt me and the men I was to serve with in the hell hole that would be known as the Western Front.

My time at Cressage was measured in weeks now and each day brought me a mixture of excitement and anxiety about the adventure which lay ahead. Doubts about the outcome of what I had committed myself to do tumbled around my head at night, fighting for my attention amongst the dreams and ideas I had nurtured for years. It was almost time to say goodbye to my family for ever.

Shortly before I left Cressage, I received a message from Lady Harnage that she wanted to see me the following Sunday afternoon, which was her usual time for receiving people she had asked to call. The elderly maid who answered the door to me looked me up and down with some disdain, although she knew perfectly well who I was. She scowled and led me into a small reception room where, with an abrupt tone of voice, she told me to wait, and then as she left added quite needlessly that I was to remember to stand up when her mistress entered.

After a few moments, the old maid opened the door and Elizabeth Harnage came in. Much to the maid's obvious irritation, as I started to get up I was asked to remain seated and the maid was dismissed. Lady Harnage, now employing the aid of a walking stick, crossed the room and sat down carefully. As a child I had simply thought that she was very old and always had been. But now the pale winter sunshine struggled through the fine Georgian window to brighten the room, and as it did so it cast a soft glow of light on the side of her face and lit up the shadow of beauty that had been her youth.

For a little while she talked of the adventure that lay ahead of me. She envied me and my opportunity and hoped that I would be able to fulfil all my dreams. Then she handed me a small book, saying that it might keep me company on my long journey and hoped that it would make an impression upon me and, with my Bible, help support my Christian faith whilst far from home. The book was Harriet Beecher Stowe's *Uncle Tom's Cabin*, and I treasure it still.

Finally the day of my departure arrived. The few possessions that I took with me were packed into a carpet bag: my working clothes, two clean shirts, two changes of underwear, socks, shaving and wash kit, hairbrush, boot-cleaning kit, knife, fork, spoon, tin mug and plate, my bible, my pen and writing paper, three books and my life's savings, which amounted to £8-14s-6¾d. I wore or had stuffed into my pockets, everything else that I was to take with me, including my railway ticket to Liverpool. After breakfast, I stepped out of Jasmine Cottage and through the grey half-light, gazed across the long field and over Plocks Brook. I thought of all that this place I called home had meant to me, of all in that unchanging scene that I knew to be familiar, my family who had been here before me, the grandparents I had never known; now I would see it no more. The chill of the morning air disturbed my thoughts and I went back inside.

Never before had I seen my mother cry, but on that cold, damp February day, the tears silently trickled down her face; a face that bore all the trials of fifty-two years' graft and the births of eight infants. She was used to seeing her children leaving home and going out into the world, but her world was relatively small. I would be the first one to go to another country and not return; the first of her children that she knew she would never see again. On that drab morning, she could never have known that I would not be the last. My mother stood with her back to the kitchen range, the heat of the fire warming her body but not her heart. I kissed her wet cheek and tasted the salt of her tears that flavoured the bitterness of the moment, the moment when I left not only my family but everything I had been and done up to that point in my life. My parents had never been demonstrative in the love they had for their children, but my mother held me, kissed my cheek and whispered words to me that she could barely speak for the tears.

The guilt for the pain I was causing her bit deeply into me that morning but I could not turn back now; I could not see that my future lay in Cressage as it had been for my father and generations before him. I was sure that it waited for me somewhere out there in the brave new world that was emerging from the Victorian era. Mother did not come to see me catch the train; that would have been too much for her to endure. I left her as I had so often seen her, standing at the kitchen table preparing food for her family.

"When you're ready, Rowland." My father's voice was matter-of-fact; I knew that this was hard for him too. He stepped out with me to Cressage station, and whilst we made our way along Wood Lane, he wished me a safe journey, a successful life and warned me not to forget to write to my mother. We joined the three or four other passengers waiting on the platform. Before long, the little GWR tank engine pulling two coaches, three cattle trucks, two grey goods wagons and the guard's van, clanked into the station and hissed steam across the platform in faint imitation of its larger cousins. No-one got out. The porters loaded a miscellany of items into the goods wagons. It was a scene I had witnessed so many times before and epitomised rural England at that time: I knew that I would miss it.

A few minutes later, the Stationmaster came along the platform towards us wearing an expression of suitable solemnity. "Good luck, Rowland. We're sorry to see you go, son. You mind that you keep safe in that far-off land." He shook my hand and then blew his whistle; the little tank engine tooted in reply. I gave my father a hug, assured him of the certainty of my venture and that I would remember to write. I stepped into the unheated third-class compartment just as, with a gentle jerk and a cloud of smoke and steam, the tank engine eased its mixed assemblage into motion. I leaned out of the window in the door and waved to my father as he stood on the platform where the steam had curled around his body, his arm raised, his cap in hand. He hadn't quite been able to say goodbye; I knew the words had stuck.

The train pulled away and I lost sight of my father. I sat down on the hard-slatted seat, my excitement tinged with sadness in the knowledge that, in all probability, I would not see my family or this lovely county ever again. The engine had barely gathered any speed when it began to slow, for the next stop was Cound Halt, barely a mile along the track, followed by Berrington and then on to Shrewsbury, where I changed for Crewe and Liverpool. It was 23rd February; my great adventure had begun.

Jane's wedding to Edwin Higginson, November 1911.
We are all gathered outside Jasmine Cottage having just returned
from Cressage church.

My father is standing on the right of the picture. Alice is seated in front of him, and on her right are Jane and Edwin. Standing between Jane and Alice is our mother, with her hand on Jane's shoulder. I am standing next to Mother behind Jane. The two little girls at the front are Nellie [in front of Jane] and Maud. Next is Lucy and the boy standing next to her with his hand on her shoulder is my brother Herbert. This is the only photograph that I have of Herbert.

My memento pencil from the Royal Show at Liverpool in 1910

(STEERAGE)

Inspection Card for Immigration Officer at Port of Arrival in Canada

Name of Immigrant........ *Rowland Hill*

Name of Ship **CANADA**........................ Sailing from...... **LIVERPOOL**

Date of sailing...... 24 FEB 1912...... Country of last permanent residence.... 24

Name appears on Manifest, page..line......

Medical Examination Stamp.	Civil Examination Stamp.	Inland Exchange Order
	CANADIAN IMMIGRATION Admitted MAR 4 1912 Portland INSPECTOR	Reads over................Ry.

VACCINATION PROTECTED

....
Ship Surgeon's Signature.   (SEE BACK)

My steerage passage card to Canada aboard the SS Canada.
The Dominion Line was still using the old forms. By 1912 we were
not supposed to be called steerage but third class passengers even
though we all knew that the shipping lines still regarded us as
profitable steerage cargo. The medical stamp and vaccination
signature was on a separate form which I had to hand in at Aylmer.

Chapter Four

"When summer's end is nighing
And skies at evening cloud,
I muse on change and fortune
And all the feats I vowed
When I was young and proud."
When Summer's End is Nighing – AE Housman

It was early evening when the train pulled into Lime Street Station, and the sky was already dark. Carrying my carpet bag, I stepped out of the carriage beneath the vast single-span arch of the station roof. I walked past the hissing, gasping London & North Western Railway engine which had pulled us from Crewe and stood for a few moments in the bitter, cold night air at the main entrance. Looking out into the gloom, I had my first glimpse of city life, a scene as remote to me as anything I could have imagined. Trams whirred past, connectors flashing on wet cables, their iron wheels squealing on the rails. Men with collars turned up and heads bent down, hands thrust deep into pockets, scurried silently by without a forward or sideways glance. The globe of white light from each gas lamp along the pavement cast a spectral halo through which the driving sleet momentarily sparkled and glistened as it twisted and swirled before being dashed to the ground, there to become part of the filthy slush which coated roadway and pathway alike.

Turning up my own collar and pulling my cap down more tightly, I stepped out from the scant shelter of the station entrance to be swallowed up in the tide of anonymous figures streaming like lemmings towards the river. The sleet lashed my face and stung my eyes. In Cressage, where everyone knew everyone else, the appearance of a stranger would not have gone unnoticed for more than a few minutes, but here in the midst of this heaving throng, I was just another nondescript hunched body amongst all the other nondescript hunched bodies moving along that bleak, unwelcoming street.

At regular intervals along the street a door would swing open. The rumbling hubbub of men talking, sometimes accompanied by piano music, laughter or shouting but always with the unmistakeable aroma of beer, would escape from within and burst into the icy air, enveloping all who happened by. Then with the closing of the door, the cadence would be snuffed out as if it had never existed. Occasionally, a man would stagger out of a doorway and with difficulty keep his balance on the slushy pavement before trying to head off in several directions at the same time; whether for home or another pub was impossible to determine. It was Friday night in Liverpool and its workforce was spending their hard-earned wages before they went home and handed over what was left to waiting wives and eager, expectant, hungry children. If they were lucky, there would be fish and chips for supper that night after all; if not, it would be the feel of their father's belt and more hunger; it was a drama acted out a thousand times in Britain's cities.

I walked on between the shallow pools of pale white light. The clatter and clanking of trams, the snatched raucous interludes from the pubs, the metallic clip-clop of hooves from horses still labouring between the cart shafts, the staccato stutter of an occasional new-fangled motor car or omnibus, all ringing in my ears; the music of the city as unfamiliar to me as a nightingale's song would be to these men.

I turned right into Hanover Street where the stream of lemmings was thinner. The friendly glow and comforting hiss of the gas lamps helped both my safety and sense of direction; I did not want to become lost in the warren of alleyways, passages and side roads which abounded my route. On each side, imposing buildings of dressed stone and red brick rose up into the dark sky broken only by grand doorways and those darkened alleys.

Before too long, I sensed that I was nearing the river and the docks. The wind seemed to have increased; the sleet battered and stung my face with renewed vigour, forcing my head down further, and though I could barely see where I was going, I could now smell the river. I had smelled the sea before, but what I smelled that night was not the sweet essence of salt borne upon the breeze but the stench of a busy port and a river polluted by its constant use as the city's drain; it was not a pleasant smell.

At length, and with some relief, I reached the docks. My first destination for that night was the shipping office of the Dominion Line, previously part of the British & North Atlantic Steam Navigation Company but now owned by the International Mercantile Marine Company group. This major shipping group included the White Star Line, a name which just six weeks later would be on the lips of the world along with that of their most famous ship, the ill-fated RMS *Titanic*.

In 1912, Liverpool docks stretched for seven miles along the river front, and as far as I could make out, I was somewhere in the middle of it all near the Pier Head. This was my first sight of ocean-going ships and the pictures I had seen of them had not prepared me for what I saw. I was dwarfed by the towering walls of iron and steel that lay silently against the quayside, tethered by their massive mooring ropes. Everything here seemed to be on a gigantic scale.

The Arctic wind whipped across the water and cut through me, breaking into my wonderment; I was cold and hungry and needed to find the shipping office. I walked further along the quayside until I came to James Street and the offices of Richards, Mills & Company, agents for the Dominion Line. The uninviting stone steps to one side of the building led down a long narrow passageway lit only by a single small gas lamp high up on the wall. The doorway at the far end opened into the spartan dimness of the steerage office waiting room, barely brighter than the passageway.

The two timid gas lamps which spluttered and hissed on walls that once were whitewashed but now a pallid fawn from years of nicotine and grime did nothing to warm the air or the cold stone slabs of the floor. The solid wooden benches around the sides were the only offering of comfort. There were two other young men of my own age already there waiting for the clerk to show some interest. Presently, he asked us our names, looked at our papers and directed us to the Company's boarding house a few streets away, with a reminder that we were to be back by 8.30 the next morning.

Having found the Dominion offices, my next priority, which was shared by the other two, was to get something to eat. I had long since finished the bread, cheese, onion and salt ham which my mother had sent with me. Earlier, I had passed two or three fish and chip shops, and although I had never eaten anything that had not been home cooked, pangs of hunger and the seductive smell of the frying were like a siren call, luring me in. The shipping clerk told us that we would pass another one on the way to the boarding house, so we made our way out of the office and back up the steps. Outside, the sleet had turned to snow.

Our footsteps crunched upon the frozen pavement as, with collars up and heads down, we followed the clerk's directions. The pale light from the small window of the chip shop shone upon the fresh snow like a beacon and we eagerly joined the queue inside. By the time it was my turn, I had witnessed the process several times. I placed a 1½d on the counter and, without having to say anything at all, was given in exchange my supper wrapped up in a hot bundle of newspaper. Reluctantly leaving the warmth of the shop, the three of us stood in the meagre shelter offered by the doorway of the adjoining dingy building and opened our precious bundles. I know that my mother would have been devastated, but I had never tasted anything quite so good in all my life as that first fish supper.

As we ate, we talked and it turned out that my two companions, Albert and Silus, were both from Lancashire and that we were all farm workers destined for Canada on the ship of the same name sailing the next day, although we were going to different parts of that immense country. We had not quite finished eating when two quite attractive young women approached us and asked if we wanted to spend some time with them; at least I think that is what they meant because I never did know exactly what they said. Especially in the late nineteenth and early twentieth century, Liverpool, like Glasgow, London and Birmingham, had its own vocabulary as well as its own distinctive dialect, all of which was totally unintelligible to anyone from outside. However, some things transcend language and this invitation was one of them. Albert and Silus clearly understood what had been said and quickly declined. Discretion being the better part of valour, I followed their example and we headed for the boarding house feeling much warmer and more comfortable now that we had eaten.

That night we slept on the floor. The boarding house provided straw-filled mattresses, each with the dubious luxury of a single, grubby horse blanket. There were about twelve people to each room, although women and children were given a separate room. As I discovered at breakfast, there had been around forty people staying that night. I did not undress. I lay on the mattress as I was, used my carpet bag as a pillow and pulled the rough blanket, stiffened from years of use, around me in an effort to keep warm. I had no sleep. A combination of my strange surroundings and the inevitable orchestral noises which accompany communal sleeping conspired to deny me rest. There were times during the night when I did dwell upon the thought that had I accepted the girls' earlier offer, whilst I would not have had any more sleep, I might at least have been more comfortable for part of the night.

Saturday 24th February 1912 dawned cold, grey, wet and windy over the drab and dank docks. It had stopped snowing. This was to be my last morning in England; by evening I would be somewhere out at sea. My mattress, the disagreeably smelling blanket and the breakfast provided of thick porridge followed by bread and scrape [beef dripping] had cost me 6½d. Together with the two men I had met the night before, I made my way back to the shipping office, and although we arrived just before 8.30, it was well past 9 o'clock before the agent arrived. By now the room was full to overflowing with hopefuls on the cusp of a new life. However, there was little cheer in the air or upon the faces of my fellow travellers. We were all leaving hardship and poverty in Britain but whether we were leaving it behind or simply exchanging it for a different version, no-one yet knew.

Whilst we were all due to sail upon the same ship, not everyone was going to Canada; some were planning to settle in America. Presently, my name was called and I paid the balance of my assisted passage and received my ticket with its all-important stamp to cover my railroad fare for the onward journey to Canada, for I was not to disembark until we arrived at Portland, Maine, in the United States. I also received my Canadian Immigrant Inspection Card upon which was noted the barest of essential details: my name; the ship I was to sail in, the SS *Canada*, port of departure, Liverpool, and that I could be found at page 9 line 24 on the ship's manifest in the event of disaster. It was here that I lost my identity for the rest of the journey; I was now simply contract ticket number 24329. My final destination was a farm near to Aylmer, a small town in Ontario on the shores of Lake Erie.

The SS *Canada* had been built at Harland & Wolff's Belfast yards and launched on 14th May 1896. She was 8,806 tons at construction, 500 feet 4 inches long and 58 feet 2 inches wide. On 1st October that year she sailed on her maiden voyage to Quebec and Montreal, arriving a week later. In 1899, she became transport ship No.69 for the duration of the Boer War. On her first passage to South Africa, she left Liverpool with 68 officers, 7 warrant officers and 1,868 NCOs and other ranks. Throughout that war she transported troops, female nurses, horses, tobacco, refugees, the wounded and the sick, backwards and forwards between Britain and the Cape. In 1909, she underwent a re-fit which increased her gross tonnage to 8,981, providing accommodation for 463 second-class and 755 third-class passengers. The re-fit had improved some elements of conditions below decks but, despite being officially designated as third class, we were still referred to in the paperwork as steerage passengers and treated accordingly by the crew; we were simply profitable cargo.

Once everyone had been processed, we were ushered out of the offices and led down to the quayside in the cold wind and freezing rain, where a small tender waited to transport us further up the River Mersey to where the ship was anchored mid-stream. It was not excitement that I felt as I stepped onto the tender that morning, but a mixture of anticipation tinged with apprehension. I had left English soil for ever; I would almost certainly never return to the land of my birth. I looked around me at the other cold, grim, disconsolate passengers crowded on to the tender; melancholy the only emotion staring back at me from their otherwise blank expressionless faces. There was no excited chatter, no happy banter. A few waved sadly to families ashore who had come to see them off; the rest just stared at nothing in particular.

From the distance, the ship looked disappointingly small for a trans-Atlantic crossing. However, as we neared her, the black bulk of steel-riveted plates with regularly spaced port holes soon towered forty feet or more above us. Once the tender was secured alongside the liner, we climbed the external stairs and entered through a small doorway in the side, where a junior officer greeted us without ceremony, giving brusque instructions to keep following the rope down the steep stairs to the steerage quarters.

Before the re-fit, our part of the ship had been one huge room, but it had now been divided up into smaller sections for sleeping, with a larger space retained as the dining area. There were twenty-four of us in my 'cabin', the bunks arranged across the floor in two blocks of twelve. Each block was two bunks high, three long and two wide, with a thin iron rod between conjoining beds. Unaccompanied women were accommodated in a separate area, as were families. Foreign passengers, that is non-British nationals, were in yet another area on an even lower deck. Our group of twenty-four comprised two Scots and an Irishman, the rest being drawn from various parts of England, including my two companions from Lancashire, though I alone was from Shropshire.

I was one of the first into the cabin and quickly secured a top bunk, staking my claim by climbing up onto the straw mattress and remaining there until everyone was settled. In addition to the regulation horse blanket, which was much cleaner than the one I had enjoyed at the boarding house the night before, the Dominion Line had provided us each with basic cutlery, a tin mug and a tin plate. Whilst everywhere was scrubbed down and spotlessly clean, the air still smelled and tasted sour. It was a mixture of cold metal, damp, sweat, vomit and disinfectant. It didn't improve.

My mother had sewn a secret pocket into my jacket in which I had hidden most of my money and my ticket, so feeling it safe to leave my carpet bag on the bunk, and the flow of passengers down the stairs having eased, I went back up on deck to look around and to get away from the stale air below, even though the air outside was far from fresh. I had expected to be able to walk around the ship or at least a reasonable amount of it and was both disappointed and surprised to find that travelling steerage meant access only to a very small area on each side.

For the next two hours or so the tenders brought more passengers until it seemed there was room for no more. As the last tender approached us, so too did a pair of tug boats, which soon had their lines secured to us. No sooner had the last person stepped aboard than the doorway was closed, the tender cast off and the ship started to move under the power of the tugs. They manoeuvred us downstream to the landing stage, where the *Canada* was once more tied up so that the second-class passengers and the last of the stores, mail, livestock and luggage could all be brought on board.

Whilst all this was going on, all the steerage passengers were rounded up and told to report to the ship's doctor, the purpose of which was a scant medical examination.

By mid afternoon, we were ready to sail and, guided by the tugs, started out on our voyage with 946 adults and 139 children on board. At the mouth of the Mersey, the tugs cast off and we turned south down the Irish Sea into the gathering darkness and rising wind. Down below, people had sorted themselves out and were beginning to strike up conversations with their travelling companions. Despite the time of year, the temperature between the decks was already uncomfortably warm and the motion of the ship in the open sea began to quickly take its toll upon those who were not good sailors.

Having never been on a ship before, I had no idea how I would react. Whilst I was on the deck, in the freshening air, I was reasonably content, but once inside and below, I knew that I would not enjoy rough weather. My stomach began to turn over; I could feel the colour drain out of my face and I felt clammy. At 7pm, the stewards brought in steaming cauldrons of a gravy stew.

The dank, acrid air, the smell of the food and the rolling motion of the ship proved too much for me and I joined the chorus of sufferers from the misery that is seasickness.

The French know it more genteelly as *le mal de mer*, but by whatever name, there is nothing quite like the malady of seasickness. There is no escape or even relief. It drains all external senses. My whole body felt as if it was being turned inside out with every roll of the ship. There were pitifully few lavatories in steerage for so many people; not that it really mattered, as only one or two sufferers were able to make anything but the feeblest attempts to reach them. It seemed that almost everyone around me was being sick, and in a very short space of time, the whole deck area echoed to the sounds of retching and vomit splattering on the iron deck. The already foul air now smelled putrid. The floor was awash with regurgitation, and anyone moving about needed the greatest of care not to slip and fall into it as the ship pitched and rolled its way down St George's Channel and through the Celtic Sea. I became numbed to my surroundings, oblivious to everything except my own misery.

If I was to be saved from this purgatory, I needed fresh air, and so I struggled up the stairway onto the meagre deck area only to find it already crowded with people either being sick or preparing to be so. I managed to reach the rails and continued to vomit, though by now it was only a vile-tasting fluid which came up. The freezing February rain was driving hard across the deck, and as it mixed with the spray and spindrift I was quickly soaked to the skin. All too soon I was at the point where, despite knowing what awaited me, I could stand the cold and the wet no longer; I had to go below once more. My head felt terrible. I was dizzy, my eyes unable to focus, my stomach felt as though I had swallowed a writhing snake. Drained from my retching, I once more clambered wearily into my bunk and, though still fully clothed, sought the sanctuary of slumber. But even though I was tired from a lack of sleep the night before, the relief I so much needed would not come. Every time I was nearly there, another bout of retching would overcome me or one of the others in the room.

I must have dozed intermittently and as Saturday became Sunday, the new day brought a new course. We came out from the lee of Ireland and what little shelter it had provided. We turned west to head into the full fury of the Atlantic storm which had turned the sea into a livid, boiling hell. The gale piled the seas up into ranks of great waves which bore down upon us relentlessly. The frothing spindrift was barely airborne before it was whipped off the top of each crest and thrown into the back of the preceding wall of water. Through my stupor, I felt the *Canada* climb the steep face of each mountainous sea, pause upon the crest as if in fearful trepidation of the descent, then crash down on the other side with a shuddering bang which reverberated throughout the ship. Had I not felt so ill, I should have feared for my safety, convinced that the ship could not withstand such punishment and that surely she must either break up or not rise from the next trough but stay on her downward slide until she hit the sea bed.

Neither happened, but as I lay rising and falling, rolling and lurching in my bunk, I could think of nothing other than the desperate need for it to end. I had ceased to care whether the ship sank or floated, just so long as that terrible motion would stop and bring me relief. I had long since emptied the last of my stomach fluids and it seemed everything else inside me as well, onto the floor and into my bed, but still I retched, heaved and spewed mercilessly. Finally, utterly spent and totally exhausted to the point of oblivion, I slept.

Time had lost all meaning, all context, but partially roused from my inertia, I had a vague recollection of the ship's rolling motion subsiding and then all being quiet and peaceful; perhaps we had sunk after all. It appeared that we had called in to Queenstown in southern Ireland to collect mail and a few more passengers. Enveloped by a sense of relief, I dropped back into unconsciousness and slept the blessed sleep of the innocent. When I awoke, it was Monday morning and we were well out into the ocean. The ship was still rolling wildly but the crashing sounds had stopped, from which I took heart that the storm had abated and we had survived. I still did not feel well, but at least I felt no worse. Hushed voices seeped through from another bunkroom, whilst further away, the sounds of talking, laughter and clunking of tin mugs and dishes drifted up from the main dining area; it seemed that some at least were good sailors. The overall impression, though, was one of quiet, and in my own bunkroom, all were either asleep or at contented rest. I made no effort to get up but closed my eyes and drifted back to sleep.

With the evening, the sea became calmer and I needed to get out on deck; the air in our quarters was rancid. In the fresh air, I began to feel better and, for the first time since Saturday morning, hungry. After an hour or so in the open air of the steerage deck, I went back below and joined the others who had now set about cleaning up the mess. The ship's crew provided the mops, buckets and disinfectant to clean up, but not the labour. Within a short space of time, we had the place looking reasonable again though it smelled like a freshly cleaned public lavatory. We were just in time for supper, which was bread, butter, cheese and some rather insipid-looking tea. However, having eaten nothing for nearly three days, it was all that I wanted.

Breakfast next morning, and every morning, was porridge, coffee, bread and butter. Tuesday, however, also brought the vaccination muster. The whole of No.1 steerage was paraded in a line, right arms bared to the shoulder, ready for the doctor's inspection. Anyone without an obvious vaccination mark was re-done. There were many objections, but the answer was simple: without the doctor's vaccination certificate, entry to both Canada and the

United States was barred. With poor humour and pallid faces, each in turn received the concoction of vaccines that flowed through a needle bigger than I had used on cattle. There were no soothing words or any pretence that this was anything but a sausage machine operation. Each needle was repeatedly used until it was too blunt to break the skin; only then was it changed. It was clear that the job was to be done as quickly and efficiently as possible, without ceremony. From time to time, at the first sight of the needle, there would be a guttural groan followed by a heavy thump as the victim, usually a big man, slumped to the floor. As if bending to retrieve a dropped glove, the doctor simply followed the man down, stuck the needle into bare flesh, pushed on the plunger until the syringe was empty, and then instructed two men in the waiting line to drag the unconscious body to one side and out of the way. The process was never intended to be delivered caringly.

The calmer seas brought swifter progress, but with the passing of sickness, it also brought a change to the general feel of steerage. The biggest men asserted their size by going to the front of the queue and taking the best of what food was on offer, often to then scurry like rats back to their bunks to sit and eat it. The opportunities for personal hygiene were neither great nor many, which did nothing for the air quality. Increasingly, now that the weather had improved, I took to the deck and spent most of my time with Albert and Silus, easily whiling away the hours with farming talk.

Although the men's and women's sleeping accommodation were separate, they were accessible to one another via stairs on opposite sides of the ship. It did not take the passengers long to discover this fact and there is no doubt that some of the young women were just as enthusiastic to exploit this discovery as were the young men, particularly after darkness fell, and the ship's night-watchman soon gave up his hopeless task of trying to ensure everyone was where they were supposed to be. Darkness also brought a slowing of the engines, reducing our progress to what seemed little more than walking pace. On one night, we stopped altogether and when I went on deck to see why, found that we were surrounded by thick sea fog. The sonorous booming of the *Canada*'s fog horn sounded every few minutes throughout the night and well into the following morning.

The voyage settled down to the regular routine of the ship, each day drawing us closer to the New World. We soon learned which of our fellow passengers were companionable, which to share a story or a joke with, which to trust and especially which to avoid.

This was a leap year and when that extra day dawned, we were over halfway across the Atlantic. The air on deck was bitterly cold, making me draw my scarf around my head to protect me from the wind that always blows at that latitude. The throbbing engines sounded a hypnotic rhythm while the ship made a steady furrow through the sea, throwing spumes of white foam out from the bow, cutting the swell with the ease of a sharp plough blade through the soil. Now and then, we would pass an occasional ice floe which had drifted down from the Arctic on the current; the first signs of the longer days in the north and the promise of the beckoning spring. Gazing from the deck at those drifting floes with great excitement and thoughts of where they had come from, I could never have imagined the appalling tragedy which awaited the RMS *Titanic* as she steered a similar course to our own across the Atlantic just six weeks later.

Of all the events in 1912, the loss of the 'unsinkable' *Titanic* with 1,503 passengers and crew must rank as the most momentous of the year, a disaster which has taken on almost mythical, and more recently, fanciful proportions in the minds of the British people. Amongst the real crew of *Titanic* were two very different but remarkable people, each endowed with extraordinary luck. Born on 30th May 1874, Charles Lightoller was the most senior crew member to survive the disaster. He had gone to sea at thirteen and within two years had been shipwrecked twice. Having survived a cyclone, a cargo room fire and malaria, in 1898 he left the sea and tried to find his fortune in the Klondike.

Unsuccessful as a prospector, he worked his passage back to England in 1900 and joined the White Star Line. He was appointed Second Officer aboard *Titanic* for her maiden voyage, and when disaster struck was responsible for loading lifeboats on the port side. Lightoller, last of the crew to leave *Titanic*, stayed too long and was sucked under. He was held against a grate until a blast of air from below blew him to the surface. During the night he was a long time in the icy water before climbing onto the upturned collapsible B with about thirty other men. Later they transferred to a lifeboat. When rescued next morning, he was the last person out of the last lifeboat to board *Carpathia*.

A Royal Navy Reservist, he served all through the Great War, during which he was twice more shipwrecked, awarded the Distinguished Service Cross and Bar and the Reserve Decoration and promoted to the rank of Commander. During the Second World War he was Mentioned in Dispatches for his actions at the evacuation of Dunkirk.

Violet Constance Jessop, often called 'Miss Unsinkable', was born on 1st October 1887 in Argentina, where as a child she contracted tuberculosis. She survived the usually fatal disease and at sixteen moved to England with her mother and five younger siblings following the death of her father. In 1910, she joined the White Star Line as a stewardess aboard the RMS *Olympic*. The following year she was working the ship when it was struck by HMS *Hawke*, a Royal Navy ship designed to ram and sink other vessels. Badly damaged, *Olympic* just managed to make it back to Southampton.

Six months later, Miss Unsinkable was aboard *Titanic*. Ordered on deck to show non-English speakers how to behave calmly when given orders, she acted out the instructions, including putting on her lifebelt and showing others how to do it. Later, she was ordered into lifeboat 16. She too was rescued by *Carpathia*.

When war came, she volunteered as a British Red Cross nurse. In 1916 she was nursing aboard HMHS *Britannic*, a converted White Star liner, when the ship exploded and sank in fifty-seven minutes. Gathering as many walking wounded patients together as she could, she helped them into a lifeboat. However, the explosion had been so severe that the crew had not been able to stop the engines, and whilst the hospital ship sank, her propellers still turned, relentlessly drawing the lifeboats into them. Unable to avoid the inevitable, Nurse Jessop jumped out of the boat but was dragged under. Like Lightoller, she was suddenly thrust upwards but struck her head on the hull. Semi-conscious, she was pulled into a lifeboat and survived yet again. She returned to the sea after the war, sailing without further mishap with White Star, Red Star and Royal Mail lines before finally retiring in 1950. She died in 1971 aged 83.

Despite the great loss of life that occurred on *Titanic*, it would pale against the magnitude of nearly 6,000 souls lost aboard the HMT *Lancastria* in 1940, the facts of which were suppressed by a government 'D' Notice for the next fifty years.

As February slipped into March, we caught another gale. Once again, seasickness took its toll on No.1 steerage, but I was surprised and greatly relieved to find that I remained unaffected. It seemed that I had gained my sea legs.

The bad weather was neither as severe nor as long-lasting as our first storm and by Saturday morning had blown over us on its eastwards track across the ocean. By dusk, we passed close by the banana-shaped Sable Island. The mood in steerage improved considerably; the atmosphere lightened as we began to sense our destinations looming. Sunday morning brought clear blue skies; the air cold and crisp in the wind that blew down from the north. More importantly, it brought land. Clearly visible in the morning light was the coast of Nova Scotia.

Within two hours we had docked at Halifax and a good many passengers left the ship here, both from steerage and second class. I would stay with the ship, though, until we reached Portland, my point of entry to Canada. Travelling to the interior of Canada in the winter was much easier from Portland because of the rail links, and thus many migrants to the Great Lakes areas went in this way. The St. Lawrence River was still frozen solid and so sailing on to Montreal was impossible.

Whilst at Halifax we took on fresh water, some mail and a few passengers, casting off before darkness fell. On Monday 4th March 1912, after some 2,800 miles of sailing, we arrived at Portland harbour and tied up alongside the wharf. However, the only people to leave the ship for some time were the second-class passengers or those steerage with American citizenship. After two more hours of waiting, the rest of us were escorted ashore and straight into a large processing shed. Here, all my papers and vaccination certificates were checked. There were no pleasantries, no 'Welcome to America, the Land of the Free', or welcome to anywhere else, for that matter. We were processed routinely, diligently but not very quickly; we were, after all, simply commodities. My number was checked and verified against my name, my papers and the ship's manifest. At immigration, we had been allocated a specific carriage letter for the train that would take us into Canada; mine was K, after which I was directed to another shed and given a much-needed hot meal of Irish stew, bread and tea. I had set foot on foreign soil for the first time in my life, but it was not quite as I had imagined it would be.

By the time everyone had been processed and fed, it was around 7pm. A shrill whistle blew to quieten the hubbub of chattering voices and clattering dishes which echoed around the shed, whereupon the whistle blower called out the letters of each carriage, starting with A. Our papers were checked on leaving the dining shed, and carriage by carriage, we followed our guides to the waiting train, which stood beside the platform in the adjoining immense station building. In here, men scurried back and forth in a hive of frenzied activity, loading the parcel wagons which made up the waiting goods traffic. Engine valves hissed scalding steam, couplings clanked and smoke belched from a dozen chimney stacks. As I walked along the platform to coach K, I thought that at least we were not being loaded onto parcel wagons; we had almost regained our identities as human beings.

The Dominion Line staff had been very careful not to lose any of us as they were responsible to the Canadian government for our safe delivery to the port of arrival, upon penalty of a substantial fine should anyone be unaccounted for. Once through immigration, though, we became the charges of the Grand Trunk Railway. Like many others, my ticket had been paid for by the Canadian government and it was now up to the GTR to deliver me in one piece. Portland was the American end of the GTR, which ran straight up into Canada and would ultimately take me all the way to Aylmer; we would, however, not stop again until Montreal, well inside Canada. I had managed to find a seat by the window and made myself comfortable. Tired, though warmed somewhat by the Irish stew, I dozed until awoken by a jolt as the train began to move. I looked at the time on my pocket watch; it was 4.12am.

Daylight broke with clear pale blue skies over the pretty countryside of Maine, and as we travelled further inland, the snow which covered everything became deeper. Occasional sleigh tracks criss-crossed between houses, woods, lakes and farms like a tangle of stretched fishing lines. Gradually the scenery became more upland in nature as we passed into New Hampshire to the east and north of the White Mountains and the immense unbroken forest which covered them, and which today is a National Park. The railroad track twisted and turned its way along the valley of the Androscoggin River, and over everything, the snow shimmered in a dazzling whiteness of reflected sunlight.

From here we travelled to Berlin Falls and then turned north-west to follow the Connecticut River which forms part of the boundary between New Hampshire and Vermont, finally crossing into Vermont at North Stratford. The afternoon wore on and the daylight became less intense, the colours of everything deepened and intensified; a precursor to the approaching darkness.

The compartment door slid open and one of the stewards came in to light our oil lamp. As he did so, he announced that we had just passed through Norton Mills and that we were now in Canada. Despite our travel weariness, we did manage a cheer; after 3,500 miles, we had at least reached the country of our dreams, if not yet our final destinations.

The news sparked some chatter amongst the eight of us in the compartment for a little while, but then, one by one, we fell silent again, each wrapped in his own thoughts once more. We had no sleeping accommodation other than where we sat, but we were fed along the way. The stewards brought Irish stew, bread, cheese, porridge, dried fruit and coffee around to the compartments at various times of the day. The passing of the hours and miles was marked only by the arrival of these victuals and the rhythmic, somnolent clickety-clack as the wheels rolled over the track. With the coming of night, the twists and turns had all but gone and the train sped along great lengths of unbending miles.

We arrived in Montreal, our first stop, more than twenty-four hours after we had left Portland. Even though it was still dark, we were all glad of the opportunity to get out of the train and stretch our legs up and down the platform, but the bitterly cold night air soon drove us back into the carriages. Shropshire is England's coldest county and I was used to low temperatures but it was much colder in Montreal than I had expected. The engine and the crews were changed here and it was half an hour before we left the station. Our direction now was west, towards the farm lands and prairies that we had travelled so far to reach.

Dawn once more brought a bright, crisp day with crystal-clear skies. The train took us through some beautiful scenery and, despite my tiredness from lack of proper sleep, I was captivated by the landscape. And then before long we were running alongside the frozen St. Lawrence River. We bypassed Kingston and Belleville and then at Brighton burst out upon the shores of Lake Ontario. Even in my imagination I had not conceived the scale of this vast frozen expanse which filled the view for the next few hours.

Having passed Whitby and Scarborough, our next stop was Toronto. It is easy to understand the very close links that Canada has with Great Britain. Even a casual look on a map will reveal familiar place names from both England and Scotland. The early settlers simply named their new communities after the ones they had left behind; it helped to keep a link with the old country where so many of their families remained.

Toronto was where the train started to unload its passengers of mainly farm workers; it was where we began to spread out into the hinterland and our allotted farms. The next stop was Stratford and it was here that I too left the train. I said goodbye to Albert and Silus, wished them well and went in search of my first connection, which took me to St. Thomas via London. At St. Thomas, my final train ride took me to Aylmer. In the fading light, I arrived at the little station which was almost hidden amongst the snowdrifts.

*Before and after – Two photographs for my mother: [above] in 1911
as a farm worker on English wages just before I left to go to Canada,
and [below] in 1913 as a well paid farm worker on Canadian wages.*

Chapter Five

"At evening when the lamp is lit,
Around the fire my parents sit;
They sit at home and talk and sing,
And do not play at anything."
The Land of Story-Books – Robert Louis Stevenson

T he trains had not been very warm and I had not taken my coat off since leaving the ship, but as I stepped out of the carriage compartment onto the platform in Aylmer, the air was so cold that it took my breath away. When I did breathe, it hurt my lungs. My English winter clothes seemed suddenly pitifully inadequate. Eagerly, I followed the half dozen or so other passengers into the shelter of the main building and rummaged in my bag for gloves and a scarf.

Within a few moments, everyone had melted away, leaving me alone in the draughty wooden booking office hall. I had been told to expect someone to meet me as the farm I had come to work on was some distance out of the town, but there was not a soul around. Through the glass panel in the doorway I looked out over the platform and tracks at the unfamiliar scene in the dwindling twilight. The deep snow immersed everything, hiding any features of the land and most of what lay on it. Only the buildings, the railway and the telegraph poles werc to be seen; the rest was a white rolling landscape of snow drifts. An involuntary shiver ran through me as I pulled my coat together more tightly and casually turned around. My audible gasp of shock took me by surprise. I was looking straight into the weather-beaten face of a man standing not six inches from me. I had not heard a sound and yet he had entered the room and walked right up behind me.

He gave a short, dismissive laugh, then said in a strange and heavy accent, "You must be young Rowland Hill?"

He was wrapped in several layers of clothes which exaggerated his powerful stocky build and included at least one animal hide of some sort and a fur hat that came down low over his forehead and ears. I could see only his eyes, nose and mouth. I couldn't tell the colour of his hair or indeed if he had any at all. The corners of his mouth twitched slightly into a faint smile as he continued, "She:kon. Yoyanerátye? I am Ehnita Okwaho Kanien'kehaka; Moon Wolf of the Mohawk, but here I am called Gray Pontiac."

I had read so much about the Native Peoples of Canada and had seen many drawings of them and their way of life. I did not think that I would meet one so soon, but the First Nation man standing in front of me looked nothing like those pictures. I was still shaken by the stealth of his entrance. "Well, Moon Wolf," I stuttered, "I've only been in Canada for two days and my Mohawk is not very good, but it's nice to meet you. Thank you for coming to the station for me."

He grunted, the faint smile vanished and he looked long and hard into my face. I realised that I was holding my breath and that I was waiting but wasn't sure for what. After what seemed a very long time, but was really only a few seconds, his bronzed face lit up in a broad beaming smile and he slapped my shoulder hard.

"That is good, Rowland. We shall get along fine, and then I will teach you Mohawk and you will understand my greeting. But for now you need more clothes. These are no good for winter in Canada." He felt the lapel of my coat and grimaced. "Come."

I picked up my carpet bag and followed him outside. It was almost dark and the freezing snow crunched beneath our feet. Small flurries of white flakes swirled around my face in the wind. It was bitter. The temperature had dropped again with the coming of night. I was expecting to walk to the farm but Gray had brought a form of transport I had only dreamed of – a dog sled. Eight

84

Huskies stood tethered in pairs to the sledge and as we approached began to howl softly, knowing they would soon be on their way again.

Gray handed me a fur hat like his own and a foul-smelling hide poncho, both of which I gladly pulled on against the cutting wind. He indicated to the seat on the sledge and passed me a thick hide blanket, which I equally gladly wrapped around me. He recovered the stake from in front of the lead pair, stepped between the runners, whistled and cracked his whip over their heads. The dogs took up the strain while Gray pushed to help break out the sled. It jerked free of the ice and began to glide over the snow with an eerie whoosshh-sshhh. I felt the man's weight as behind me he jumped onto the runners, but the dogs never faltered.

It was an hour later before the team pulled us into the farm yard; I was very glad I had not had to walk. Gray took me to the bunkhouse which would be my home for the foreseeable future and introduced me to the three other workers there. He told me that Mr Edwards, the farm owner, would see me the next day but for now, it was time to eat. A long table stood at one end of the room and the five of us sat down as the food was brought in from the farmhouse. I was ravenous, having not eaten since breakfast on the train, and the pot of steaming hot stew smelled and tasted wonderful. Tired out, that night I slept like never before.

Aylmer in Ontario, not to be confused with the town of the same name in Quebec which is now a suburb of Ottawa, is a small village built around Catfish Creek some one third of the way along the northern shore of Lake Erie and seven miles from the lake itself. Although significantly further south than my home in Britain, Aylmer has a continental climate and without the warming influence of sea currents, experiences much lower winter temperatures than I was used to.

The settlement was founded in 1817 when John van Patter, an emigrant of Dutch descent from over the border in New York State, obtained 200 acres of land and became the first settler. During the 1830s a general store was opened and village plots were sold. The village was originally called Hodgkinson's Corners because of the location of Philip Hodgkinson's business. Later American settlers also from rural neighbouring New York State renamed it Troy after a village on the Hudson River. Unhappy with the American connection, in 1835 the community officially named it Aylmer after Lord Aylmer, the then Governor-in-Chief of British North America, although for a time, the north of the settlement was known as Walkerton, after local businessman George Walker.

Its easy access to Lake Erie had enabled it to become the marketing centre for the rich agriculture and timber-producing area of this part of the northern shore. By 1880, Aylmer had developed saw and flour mills, a foundry, a pork-packing house, a milk cannery and a shoe factory, along with many smaller businesses. Until electricity arrived in 1886, many of these industries were powered by the water from Catfish Creek.

When I arrived there in 1912, it was a thriving prosperous community of some 2,000 people, having benefited greatly from the coming of the Great Western Air Line in 1873, part of which I had travelled along in the final stages of my journey. In the days before aeroplanes, an air line was simply a railway which was built as straight and flat as possible along its length, even though that route might not necessarily be the easiest one to have taken. The rationale behind it was that the shortest distance between two points is a straight line and, then as now, it was all about speed and time, even if the time savings were small in the overall scheme of things.

I was to learn from Gray that John van Patter's land acquisition, like almost all such acquisitions in the early days of settlement, did not mean the purchase of the land from the First Nations but simply its annexation; the government or the settlers just took it. The peoples of the First Nations believed that no-one owned the land, that it was part of the world and it belonged to everyone and everything that lived upon it. It was a concept that the European settlers never understood and led to the widespread exploitation of the indigenous tribes. Nevertheless, despite that fact, on the whole, the relationship between the early settlers in Canada and the peoples of the First Nations was a lot less fractious and violent than it was south of the border.

An irresistible and lethal combination of factors led to three hundred years of intermittent war in America from 1622 until as late as 1924 between the invading European settlers and the First Nations who sought to defend their homes, their families and their way of life. There was the seemingly unending stream of people arriving on the east coast whilst wagon trains and then the railroad carried them ever further westward, squeezing and displacing the tribes, occupying their hunting grounds and their sacred sites. The settlers created an insatiable appetite for the resources they found, which were exploited and squandered without relief, including most of those that sustained the indigenous peoples, such as the buffalo, which was slaughtered almost to the point of extinction. Added to the mix was a general contempt for the people and their way of life which revolved around and was at one with nature and the land that had nurtured them for thousands of years.

With the inevitability of the turning earth, leaders amongst the protagonists came and went. Just a few, particularly amongst the Peoples, were luminaries in their cause and have become the subject of folklore, myth and even reverence, their deeds passing down the generations in an oral tradition. Over the three hundred years of sporadic warfare there were many battles and many atrocities. There can be few who have not heard of the Battle of the Little Big Horn, where, on 25th June 1876, Lt. Col. George Custer's battalion of the 7th Cavalry was completely annihilated, mainly by Crazy Horse's Sioux. The remaining battalions under the command of Major Reno and Captain Benteen fared little better although casualties were not as great.

During 1876 and 1877 the Lakota Sioux, the Northern Cheyenne, the Arapaho and the Dakota Sioux combined to fight what became known as the Great Sioux War, of which the Little Big Horn in Montana was both the climax and effectively the end. The fight had been, as so often, about the Peoples being denied access to their traditional hunting grounds, this time the Black Hills of North Dakota. After the battle, Sitting Bull was exiled to Canada and the great gathering that had defeated Custer dispersed, with many drifting back to the reservations.

Having returned to the United States some years later, Sitting Bull was ordered to be arrested for endorsing the holding of the Ghost Dance. However, the two Native American policemen sent to arrest him killed Sitting Bull instead. Rather than renew the conflict, the rest of the tribe left the Standing Rock reservation and joined Red Cloud at Pine Ridge. It was there that Major Whitside, perhaps significantly of the 7th Cavalry, directed them to Wounded Knee. Here they were ordered to be disarmed, but Black Coyote, Sitting Bull's deaf-mute son, refused to give up his rifle, which in the ensuing struggle, accidentally went off. The soldiers opened fire on the now unarmed group of mainly old men, women and children. Those who managed to run away were hunted down and shot. In all, around 300 people were massacred that day. Even by the standard of treatment meted out to the Native Peoples, this was an appalling atrocity and remains a stain upon the United States of America and the 7th Cavalry in particular.

The history of the treatment of the First Nations by successive American governments can be summed up as a catalogue of injustices and betrayals. The declared aim of the government was, and perhaps still is, to destroy the culture, religion and way of life of the Native Peoples. Congress dealt with the Little Big Horn affair by threatening to suspend all food supplies to the Sioux reservations unless they ceased all hostilities and ceded the Black Hills to the government. In 1980, the Supreme Court declared the land had been taken without proper compensation. The Sioux Nation declined the compensation, insisting instead on their right to occupy their land. The dispute remains unresolved.

The milk cannery in Aylmer was the home of Dominion Canners, which had been established in 1879 and by 1894 was the third largest of its kind in Canada. During 1912, the company built a new factory at a cost of $120,000 to expand its condensed milk business, making it the largest of any such in the country. The company also canned fruit, vegetables and meat, and in 1940 established Bird's Eye frozen foods. In 1956 it sold out to Del Monte, which, three years later, closed down the operations in Aylmer for good, with the consequent loss of jobs.

Gray Pontiac was the charge hand on the farm. It was unusual at that time for a full-blooded First Nation native to hold such a position of authority, but Edwards had clearly seen in him the skills that were needed for the job. I had started to read *Uncle Tom's Cabin* on my journey and then finished it in the long evenings on the farm. As with my earlier readings of Tom Sawyer and Huckleberry Finn, so much of what I read was beyond my experience and as such I was not saddled with any of the prejudicial baggage from history, consequently I gave no thought to Gray's background; he was simply the man in charge of me and my daily work and the man who brought me my wages at the end of each week. Although certainly tough, he was a hard worker and well respected. He was also a man I could talk to, ask questions of, share work problems and ideas with. He became my friend and a man I had the greatest respect for. We did see Mr Edwards every day as he oversaw everything on the farm, but his orders were given to us through Gray.

Edwards's farm seemed immense compared with Preece's back in Cressage. Although it was not particularly big by Canadian standards, it extended to well over 7,500 acres, which is a little over thirty square kilometres and which provided summer grazing for the cattle, hay and winter feed crops, with the rest growing grain of one variety or another. The farm buildings were certainly much larger than anything I had been used to and because of the size of the holding, several bunkhouses were built at strategic points to save the workforce the time of having to travel to and from the farm each day.

After I had seen Mr Edwards on my first morning, Gray lent me some clothes better suited to the harsh Canadian winter until I could get into town, change my money and buy my own. When I did, the exchange rate was £1 to $1.72 Canadian dollars. He then took me to the cattle sheds and explained what my role would be. My main job would be the feeding, milking and cleaning out of the huge herd of dairy cattle. Almost all of the milk from the herd went to the creamery to be turned into condensed milk and exported all over the world. Even though there was electricity on the farm, all the milking was done by hand and it took a team of twelve dairymaids together with me and the head dairyman, Mr Tilling, three hours to milk the herd each morning and evening. I had thought that I was quick at hand milking but those dairymaids were like greased lightning.

I soon settled down to the routine at the farm, which, as spring approached and the days lengthened, included ploughing, harrowing and sowing. We had a stationary steam engine to thresh the grain but the motive power for the fields was supplied by teams of horses. These wonderfully gentle creatures stood nearly six feet high at the shoulder and were immensely strong. They had to work hard, especially during spring, summer and autumn, but they were all very well cared for. There were thirty-four work horses which were harnessed in pairs and, together with the family's pony for the trap and Mr Edwards's several riding horses, they made up the stable. Mr Fotherton, helped by Tom and Venn the stable lads, was always kept busy with the horses for each day's work. He was a man of about fifty, but I never knew his Christian name nor heard anyone call him anything other than Mr Fotherton.

I had learned to ride as a child but here it took on a whole new meaning. After walking, riding was the main mode of transport, and until the snow came, every opportunity was taken to go anywhere by horse because the farm was so big. Consequently, before that first summer was past, I had become a very accomplished rider. Gray helped me a great deal with many things whilst I was on the farm and improving my horsemanship was one of them. However, his own skills were remarkable; to this day, I have never seen anyone ride better or more naturally. He showed me some of the tricks and skills he had learned as a young boy for hunting bareback, and all I could do was watch in awe. These people were so much at one with their surroundings, including their innate relationship with animals.

The inventor of the telephone, Scottish-born Alexander Graham Bell, started life in Edinburgh on 3rd March 1847. At the age of 23, he came to Canada with his parents. They settled in Ontario and thus, thanks to him, by 1912 almost all the farms and larger houses in the Aylmer area had a telephone; it was where he had tested his invention. The Edwards farm was no exception. My interest in the workings of the telephone continued to grow and what I had already learned about it was to come in very useful before too long.

There was so much that was new to me; I was enjoying my work and the days of 1912 just rolled by. News of the *Titanic*'s sinking reached us some five or six weeks after my arrival. 6th June brought the eruption of the Alaskan Peninsula volcano Novarupta in what would prove to be the largest volcanic explosion of the twentieth century, releasing thirty times more magma than Mount St. Helens would do sixty-eight years later. In November, the American people elected Woodrow Wilson as their 28th President.

I got on well with the other single men on the farm and we made a good team. In addition to the two stable boys, who lived at home, there was Olaf the Norwegian, Frank and Percy, both from Somerset, and Alwyn from Bethesda. There were other workers on the farm too, mostly married. Some were much older and skilled in their areas and, as with Mr Tilling and Mr Fotherton, I never knew them by anything but their surnames. The dairymaids who helped with the milking all lived at home as they were mostly single girls, although a few were married women. As the months went by, I became very friendly with Iwan Edwards, the farmer's eldest son, who was the same age as me. It was a friendship that would last far into the future.

The long summer days in Aylmer brought both hard work and pleasure. The dairy herd was put out to the fields as soon as there was enough grass, only coming in for milking, and so I spent much more time working on the land. I learned a lot about farming on this vast scale and how the Great Lakes formed their own weather systems. Until it settles upon the 49th parallel, the border between Canada and the United States meanders considerably from east to west. With the exception of Lake Michigan, which lies wholly within America, the border runs roughly along the centre of each of the other four lakes. Aylmer is sandwiched between Lake Erie and Lake Huron, about 110 miles east of Detroit. The proximity of the lakes create long periods of extreme cold and snow in winter followed by fairly hot, sunny summers with moderate rainfall, which makes for ideal growing conditions.

Late August brought the first signs of the fading summer. The days began to grow shorter and the evening air held a chill. The harvest became the focus of everyone's attention. Once the morning milking was done, the byres cleaned and the milk made ready for collection by Dominion Canners, I joined the teams in the fields to get the crops in. We had already gathered the hay earlier in the year, but now it was time for the grain; wheat, oats, barley, peas and, most importantly, maize.

Of all the things that were new to me on the farm, maize was the most impressive. I had never seen this crop before, although I had read about it. In Ontario it was grown by the mile; it is the indigenous crop of the Americas. When Christopher Columbus landed in 1492, he wrote that he saw fields of maize that stretched eighteen miles. It was the staple diet of the Native Peoples, who were so good at growing it that little has changed in its production since then. Although several varieties are grown, depending upon the purpose to which the crop will be put, the two principal varieties used today are the Flint and the Dent, which are the same two varieties that the First Nation tribes have grown for more than 500 years.

We grew maize on the farm both to sell and as winter feed for the cattle. We were, as far as possible, self-sufficient in winter feed stuffs, for the snow and ice were so great that shipping in large quantities of animal feed during the depths of winter was simply impractical.

Maize is a remarkable crop and the skill to grow it was learned by the early settlers from the First Nation tribes who farmed it. In 1912, Ontario agricultural land values stood at $1.25 and so after all production costs had been taken into account, the profit per acre of maize was around $34, which made a very nice return for farmers. I certainly could not complain; in England, I had earned around 10/- a week working some seventy hours. Now, I earned that in a day. I was paid 40 cents an hour, which was worth around 10d in sterling at the time. For a twelve-hour day, I received $4.80 or 10/-. At today's value that would be about £315.55 a week. It may not seem a great deal today, but in 1912 I considered myself to be very well paid. I was earning around three times the wages that my father was earning back home in Shropshire.

On 8th October, the tiny state of Montenegro declared war on Turkey and brought conflict to the troubled Balkans. Serbia, Greece and Bulgaria were allied to Montenegro and all sought to free themselves from the Ottoman Empire and to secure self-government for the Christian populations in European Turkey. The war would last until May the following year. Although it all seemed very distant and irrelevant to me, it was reported in the newspapers throughout that autumn. At the time, none of us could have understood what it portended.

With the crops safely gathered in, it was time to relax and enjoy the harvest festivals. Saturday night brought the long-awaited barn dance at the farm. Mrs Edwards and her helpers served us more plates of food than I had ever seen, all of which was washed down with plenty of local beer, despite the pressures from the prohibition movement which was gathering pace at the time. The fiddles and banjos played and we danced with the milkmaids and the girls who had come from neighbouring farms. We had had barn dances at home, but not like this one and I could not remember when I had enjoyed myself as much; and there would be another one next week and the week after at other farms. There was a long cold isolating winter ahead, so we socialised with our neighbours whilst we could.

The Carling brewery was not many miles away at the town of London and not long after arriving at the farm, I had tasted this very light, yellow-coloured beer which was similar to what fifty years later would be known in Britain as lager. It was very different to the hoppy Shropshire beer that I was used to, but I soon got to like it. Prohibition was introduced into Ontario in 1916, but export was an exception and it seems that not all the beer destined to cross the river to Detroit actually made it there! The law, which was widely abused, was finally repealed in 1927.

Gray had guided me in buying good-quality winter clothes and as the temperatures began to steadily drop I was glad of my investment. In November, the first snows of the winter began to fall and stayed to lay down the foundation for what was to come. Each storm that swept out of the Arctic brought fresh snow, which, aided and abetted by the bitter wind that drove the swirling, blinding mass of flakes across the frozen face of Lake Huron, steadily built up in drifts. It covered Aylmer and everything that lay around until away from the town only the trees along the frozen watercourses, the telegraph poles and scattered homesteads could be seen protruding from the expanse of white wilderness. The vast fields, which only a few weeks earlier had flaunted their seas of waving golden grain and forests of emerald maize, were lost without trace. Somewhere beneath that endless waste, the ground lay dormant, resting, awaiting the far-off call of spring.

Moving about beyond the farm buildings became increasingly difficult and travelling any distance was hopeless without a dog sled. The attractiveness of my surroundings was everything that I had imagined and more, but the wind and the cold were beyond my comprehension. Toronto is more or less on the same latitude as the Italian city of Florence, and so although in Aylmer I was considerably further south than in Cressage, without the benefit of the warm tropical waters that wash the shores of Britain, the winters here brought bitterly cold weather. The treacherous snow gleamed alluringly bright as far as the eye could see, and with every step I took, my snow shoes crunched and crushed their way across the crystal plain, but without winter clothing, the wind would cut you in half and snuff the life out of you in moments. These were short, cloudless, perfidious days, when the elements conspired. A crisp carpet of sparkling spangled stars danced across the snow, brightening the cheerless timorous sunlight, while the frozen air was so cold and painful to breathe it would liquidise the lungs before convulsive retching would rip them out of the chest of anyone who stayed ill-equipped too long in its presence.

When the following spring brought the news of the tragic loss of Captain Scott's expedition to the South Pole and the discovery of their bodies just eleven miles from a food depot, I understood something of the intensity and misery of the cold which those men had endured and had, ultimately, succumbed to.

During the winter there was always work to be done indoors, harnesses and other equipment to be mended, sacks to be sewn, doors and windows to be repaired against the weather, and always the fight to keep the water flowing and the fodder troughs full for the cattle in the byres.

We did, though, have a little more spare time in the winter months, and some nights sitting in the bunkhouse by the light of the oil lamps listening to the wind moaning outside, Moon Wolf kept us entertained and enthralled with stories and folklore handed down through generations of Mohawk families. Part of the Iroquois people, he told stories of the heroic deeds of his forebears in struggles against other tribes, of the relationship the peoples of the First Nations have with nature and their surroundings, of their customs and beliefs. He also honoured his promise and taught me some of the Mohawk language. As a result, I learned that on that first evening at the railway station, he had welcomed me with a customary Mohawk greeting and then asked me how I was.

At home, we had always had guns so that we could shoot pigeon and rabbit for the pot. However, out here, hunting took on a whole new meaning. Gray taught me some of his hunting skills and I learned the signs left by different animals, their footprints, the significance of their tracks and how to trap them.

Occasionally, life produces an experience which, be it good or be it bad, is imprinted upon the consciousness of the brain, to remain there forever, crystal clear, neither altered nor faded by time. For me, the first of these experiences happened in the early hours of a January night in 1913. It wasn't so much that I had heard the restlessness of the cattle as that had I sensed their unease. The rhythmic breathing and contented snores of the others in the bunkhouse told its own story, but something had disturbed me and I needed to see what was troubling the animals. In the pitch dark of the room, I quietly got up and pulled on my warm hide trousers, coat and fur hat, picked up my gloves and boots and silently crept across the wooden floor to the door. As I reached for the latch I felt a hand grip my shoulder and heard a voice whisper, "You sensed it too, Roly. We'll make a Mohawk of you yet." Moon Wolf, also sensing something, had heard me get up and had been waiting for me. I had thought he was asleep with the rest of them, but I wasn't surprised at his vigilance.

In the inner porch, we pulled our boots on then wrapped sheepskin scarves around our mouths before stepping outside. The icy Arctic air blew over us in a gentle sigh. The frost was intense; the snow strangely silent beneath our feet. The bright silver disk of the full moon cast a ghostly spectral jumble of half-light and shadows over the creamy frozen landscape. As we left the farm yard, I looked up into the northern sky and beheld a sight I had only ever heard of, the Northern Lights, the aurora borealis.

The iridescent shades of blue and green, yellow, azure, violet, indigo and vermillion swirled and danced, shimmered and flashed, ebbed and flowed in gyrating patterns across the sky. I was struck motionless, gazing at this wonder of the natural world. I could never have begun to imagine the immense beauty of what I was witnessing.

I'm not sure how long I stood there for, mesmerised by that wondrous display, but after a time my brain began to register a sound that struck an ancient primordial chord somewhere deep inside me. My ears strained as Gray stepped silently forward, and then it came again; the most chilling, evocative, captivating sound on earth – the distant, long mournful howl of a wolf; the very encapsulation of the wild. It drifted eerily down the wind from somewhere to the north, wrapped around us, then faded away. I felt the cold fingers of the soft breeze caress the exposed skin of my cheeks, and with it once more came that plaintive call, spilling over us, drawing us into its embrace. Then an answer echoed around the buildings, and from a wolf which was very close to where we stood. I was suddenly startled out of my reverie by its very nearness and felt the hairs on the back of my neck rise; my pulse quickened as adrenalin surged through my veins. I knew now what had disturbed the cattle.

Although my senses were acutely heightened by the closeness of the wolves, I was intensely excited by the thrill of being a living, breathing part in a scene that was as old as the land. The seductive transience and ethereal majesty in the restless astral lights juxtaposed strangely upon me with the danger and closeness of these wolves; the embodiment and very essence of the frozen north.

We moved silently around the sheds, checking that they were still secure, searching the snow for the padded prints of those prowling intruders. If ever a man was aptly named, it was Moon Wolf, for he was as much a part of the night as were the wolves and the lights. Walking with soundless stealth just a little in front of me, he dropped to the ground on one knee and beckoned me do the same. Barely visible to the untrained eye, there upon the hard icy snow, he showed me the unmistakeable tracks of a wolf. At about five inches square for the front pad and a little narrower for the hind pad they were much bigger than the tracks of its cousin, the mountain coyote. This was a big animal.

I had of course been told that in the depths of winter, when their natural prey is hard to find in the wild, the wolves are driven out of the forests by hunger to risk coming closer to man, their great persecutor. Moon Wolf lifted his head and looked hard towards the nearest field. In the half-light I followed his gaze though I could see nothing but the rolling drifts. After a few moments, he touched my arm but did not point. My eyes had now grown accustomed to the strange light and there, not fifty yards away, almost invisible against the speckled silver of the snow, stood a huge grey wolf looking straight back at his namesake. He was a splendid animal, and behind him in a shallow dip were three others. There was no fear in these animals, masters of their environment, but nor was there any food for them at the farm that night. No more than a passive bystander, I looked on as the Mohawk and the wolf watched each other intently, sharing a silent motionless understanding. There was a communication between them, a common bond born of this land which had passed down through the generations of native man and native wolf alike.

Presently, the wolf lifted his head and let out that long slow eerie howl that can either excite or strike fear into the heart, turning blood to ice. As the echo floated away across the snow, he half turned, paused, looked back for a few moments longer, then loped away, followed by the others. I soon lost them to the night, but I knew my companion hadn't for he stayed watching for several more minutes, until he too turned and said, "Your first real meeting with the wolves, Roly. You enjoyed their visit? They are fine creatures, but settlers do not try to understand the wolf; they prefer to kill him. You are different; that is good."

It was one of only a few occasions that he said anything to me which betrayed the pain felt by the peoples of the First Nations at the loss of their lands and which, much later, I came to more fully understand.

For me, that night was the crowning experience of my time in Canada. Although I would see the lights many times and see and hear other wolves, their mournful howl floating across the landscape, nothing would ever quite match the first time on that night. These remarkable animals use their call to communicate with each other and they can hear it up to six miles away. Across the vast forests and frozen wastes of Canada, it is their telephone system.

It took about two weeks for my letters to be delivered to Jasmine Cottage and another two weeks for my mother's replies to reach me, so although I wrote regularly, my letters tended to be compiled over a few days before being posted, knowing that it would be a month or more before I received a reply. I told my family about the wolves and of all the other things that I was doing and seeing. In turn, Mother kept me up to date with all that was happening back home.

My brother Herbert had left school the previous summer and was now working on Preece's farm with Dad. Maud and Nellie were both doing well at school and Lucy and Alice were both still in service, Jane having left after she married. Lady Harnage hoped that I was enjoying life in Canada. This was news at a very domestic family level, whilst other news from the newspapers at home and Canada began increasingly to cast a long shadow.

The telephone had become immensely important to all the farms and no more so than in the depths of winter. During a particularly fierce storm, the overhead line to the house had broken away from one of the poles. The weight of ice had been too much and the line had snapped. There was no prospect of getting anyone from the telephone company for days, but Iwan, knowing of my interest in telephones, suggested to his father that I be allowed to try repairing it.

In the biting wind and searing cold, Iwan and I worked all day on the broken line, finally managing to restore the connection. Mr Edwards was delighted; the news spread quickly to other farms, and over the course of that winter Iwan and I carried out many running repairs which lasted until the engineers could get out and make permanent fixes. The upshot of all this was that the telephone company gave me some formal training on the system so that I would be ready to help out again the following winter if necessary. At that time, the telephone was still a new technology and few people had any idea how it worked. A farm worker who knew about telephones was so unusual that the company took full advantage of my enthusiasm and welcomed the help I was able to give to the isolated farms in the harshness of the winter months.

For the most part, 1913 followed much the same routine as had my first year on the farm, although by now I felt fully settled in to life in Canada and was thinking about being able to apply for my own 160 acres of land. However, I was also coming to the realisation that those 160 acres would not be of prime arable land such as we had at Aylmer, but rough prairie pasture far to the west. It was food for thought over the coming winter months of 1913/14.

Whilst the troubles of Europe seemed very far away from Aylmer, it was impossible to ignore the reports of the continued unrest in the Balkans. Despite a peace treaty in August, unrest continued and on October 17th, Serbia invaded Albania. An item of more peaceful news was reported towards the end of 1913 when the newspapers were full of the opening of the Panama Canal and the end of the hazardous journey around Cape Horn for ships passing between the two great oceans.

On the farm in Canada with some of the horses and a couple of milkmaids. That's me on the left holding the big white hat. Tom is next to me and Mr Fotherton holding the horse on the right and Alwyn at the back

Joe [left] with Iwan's brother, Al, in a post-war picture taken by Iwan showing Bunkhouse B3 behind them.

Chapter Six

"For all we have and are,
For all our children's fate,
Stand up and take the war.
The Hun is at the gate!
Our world has passed away,
In wantonness o'erthrown."

For All We Have and Are 1914 – Rudyard Kipling

There are few years which resonate so deeply and have impacted upon the world so much as 1914. Yet for most people, it started in much the same way as so many others had done. On the farm, the winter snow and ice finally melted away and we were busy with the spring sowing again. The lush grass came through and the cows were put out to graze. The sunshine warmed and brought the long days of summer. The crops grew well and a good harvest was forecast. My mother's latest letter arrived towards the end of June and spoke of the beautiful weather being enjoyed at home too.

But in the Balkans, trouble lurked once more. On the morning of 28th June, the city of Sarajevo was preparing for the visit of Archduke Franz Ferdinand, the heir to the Austro-Hungarian Empire, together with his wife, Sophie, Duchess of Hohenberg. Also preparing for their visit that morning was nineteen-year-old Bosnian Serb Gavrilo Princip. Little could he and his co-conspirators have known that before lunchtime they would have set in motion a chain of events which would change the world forever in ways far beyond their possible contemplation.

The motivation which lay behind the plot to assassinate the Archduke was the desire that Austria's South Slav provinces became part of Yugoslavia. The first attempt on Franz Ferdinand's life at 10.10 that morning had failed and it was feared the plot would come to nought. However, Princip had remained undetected amongst the crowd and, seizing the moment of an unexpected opportunity less than an hour later when the royal motorcade took a wrong turning, he shot the Archduke and his wife Sophie at close range, killing them both. The Duchess was an unintended victim. Princip's second target was the Governor of Bosnia and Herzegovina, Oskar Potiorek. The seal on the door to Armageddon had just been broken.

The assassination plot, orchestrated by the secret terrorist organisation 'Union or Death', better known as 'Black Hand', was carried out with the assistance of the Serbian military intelligence and with the knowledge and approval of both the Russian Ambassador to Belgrade, Nikolai Hartwig, and the military attaché, Viktor Artamonov.

Austrian Foreign Minister Count Leopold von Berchtold and Chief of Staff General Baron Franz Conrad von Hötzendorf, together with others in the Austrian government, had long wished to wage war against Serbia, and Franz Ferdinand's assassination was too good an opportunity to miss. However, there was a substantial obstacle standing in the way of such a declaration upon Serbia: Russia. A close ally of the Balkan Kingdom and France, Imperial Russia had to be deterred from becoming involved. Thus, before pressing the case with his own Emperor, Berchtold wanted the assurance that Germany, Austria's only real European ally, would support them. On 5th July, he received the personal assurance of the Kaiser and his chancellor, von Bethmann-Hollweg, "…that Germany would stand behind her [Austria] as an ally and a friend." This assurance would later become known as 'the blank cheque valid against the resources of the whole German Empire'.

Eighty-four-year-old Austrian Emperor Franz Joseph was an experienced campaigner in European politics and remained cautious and sceptical of the Kaiser's assurance. Before committing his country to war, he sent his Berlin ambassador, Count Marish Szögyeny, to see Wilhelm. None of the German Service chiefs or senior ministers of state were present during the pivotal luncheon meeting at which the Kaiser reiterated his commitment to support Austria. The following day, though, Wilhelm did make time to tell Admiral Alfred von Tirpitz, who was holidaying in Switzerland, "I do not believe in any serious warlike developments. The Czar will not place himself on the side of regicides. Besides, neither Russia nor France is prepared for war." Outwardly convinced that matters would not escalate any time soon, the Kaiser left on his gold and white yacht for a twenty-day cruise around the Norwegian fjords.

Austria was determined to crush Serbia; Russia was determined that it should not. To allow it to do so would make Austria the dominant power in the Balkans. Germany, undoubtedly the best prepared and equipped of the Central Powers for a war, was confident that its military might supporting Austria would prevent the Russians from acting to support Serbia. The Austro-German strategy was to keep the dispute confined to Austria and Serbia and not to draw in the other European powers, thus ensuring Austria's success.

Wilhelm had become Kaiser upon the early and tragic death of his father, Frederick III, on 15th June 1888. It remains that but for Frederick's untimely death from laryngeal cancer after only fifty-five days as Kaiser, the history of the twentieth century might well have been so very different. Married to Princess Victoria, the eldest child of Queen Victoria, Frederick was a Liberal and a great admirer of Britain. He hoped to lead Germany to a less autocratic future, with the parliament sitting in the Reichstag exerting a greater influence in the country's politics. Wilhelm, though, did not share his father's aspirations and took his country, and ultimately himself, towards a destructive and much less attractive destiny.

Jealous of Britain's industrial, trading and imperial supremacy around the world during the nineteenth century, Wilhelm greatly expanded Germany's own industrial output and increased her overseas territories, especially in Africa, to feed that growing demand. One of the businesses which Wilhelm turned to was the vast Krupp iron and steel works based at Essen in the heart of the Ruhr, and he made it the mainstay of munitions production. Founded in 1812 by Frederick Krupp, the firm developed a secret method of producing fine quality steel. The Krupp Works would continue to be inextricably linked to German munitions production until 1945.

Unlike Britain, Germany had had compulsory military service for many years, and with a large standing army and a navy that was second in the world only to the Royal Navy, she was much better prepared and equipped for a large-scale war. Indeed, most European countries other than Britain had some form of compulsory peacetime military service.

The summer of 1914 brought particularly pleasant weather across Europe and many of its peoples were either holidaying or enjoying the July sunshine wherever and whenever possible. The French danced in front of the public bandstands in their towns and cities, went to the country or to the Mediterranean coast; Paris was empty. The British held garden parties, played tennis on the lawn or, like the French, took a train to the seaside to paddle, bathe and listen to the band. Most remained blissfully unaware of the momentous events that were unfolding in the palaces and government offices of Europe.

Since the assassination, Austria, emboldened by Germany's support, became increasingly belligerent towards Serbia and on 23rd July handed its ultimatum, drafted by Berchtold, to the Serbian government, giving only forty-eight hours for the acceptance of terms which were deliberately designed to be unacceptable. Two days later, and with only minutes to spare before the deadline expired, Serbia delivered its response, which acceded to all the demands bar the two which compromised its sovereignty.

The Kaiser was acutely aware of the Triple Entente Cordiale, brokered by Edward VII between Great Britain, France and Russia, together with the latter's treaty with France, and was content to accept Serbia's reply. Berchtold, however, supported by General von Moltke, the German Chief of the Imperial General Staff, was not. Von Moltke argued that with the fine weather, "...the unusually favourable situation should be used to strike...France's military situation is nothing less than embarrassed, and Russia is anything but confident; moreover the time of year is favourable."

Germany's military leadership had been preparing for a European war for many years with the specific aim of neutralising both France and Russia. Von Moltke's predecessor, Count Alfred von Schlieffen, had devised an ambitious plan to invade and conquer France within weeks and then turn the full might of Germany's forces upon Russia, which, although boasting an army of six million men, was thought to be unable to readily mobilise such a force. The Schlieffen Plan, which took some eight years from 1897 to perfect, was accepted by the German military high command as the ideal method of achieving its aims against France and Russia; all it needed was the opportunity to put it into operation. That opportunity had arrived.

In 1839, Britain, along with other European nations including Germany, had signed a pact to guarantee Belgium's perpetual neutrality. Despite this, Schlieffen's plan relied upon Belgium as a back-door entrance to France, so avoiding the substantial French defensive positions on the Franco-German border. It also anticipated speed, superior forces and a supine Belgian army. Paris was to be surrounded within weeks and the invasion completed shortly thereafter. The strategy worked rather like a revolving door. Centred around the Lorraine city of Metz close to the post-1870 French border, the right [northern] wing of the invading forces would sweep across Belgium, turn south through France, passing between Paris and the Channel coast and then, once south of Paris, turn east back towards their own advancing troops of the left [southern] wing coming into France through Alsace and Lorraine, thus completing the circle and entrapping the retreating French army in a huge pincer movement. Schlieffen, the great military tactician, had studied Hannibal's successful strategy at the Battle of Cannae in 216 BC against the much stronger Roman forces and had used it as the basis upon which his plan was founded.

Germany's chancellor, von Bethmann-Hollweg, was convinced that Britain would not go to war over the 1839 treaty. The gamble was that Britain, with a very small standing army of only 160,000 men designed for Empire peace-keeping duties rather than a major European war, would not enter the conflict over a breach of Belgium's neutrality, and whilst there was an Entente Cordiale between Britain and France, there was not a treaty of mutual support in time of war.

In the ten years since the Schlieffen Plan had been finalised, however, much had changed in Europe. Both the French and the Russians had considerably strengthened their armies. The Russians, with French money had also built thousands of miles of railways to enable a much swifter mobilisation of its troops, and the Italians, felt by Germany to be allies, were much less inclined to war if Britain was involved. As he lay dying on 4th January 1913, von Schlieffen had reportedly urged, "It must come to war...make the right wing strong." But unable to match Franco-Russian defence spending, von Moltke had already been forced to alter parts of the plan, most significantly by taking troops from the northern right wing in order to strengthen the southern left wing against a French counter-attack through Alsace.

Russia's unwillingness to see Serbia invaded compelled Foreign Minister Sazonov to warn Germany, "Russia cannot allow Austria to crush Serbia and become the predominant power in the Balkans." The Kaiser, at last recognising that Austria's actions were endangering the peace and stability of Europe, somewhat belatedly urged caution and further discussions to resolve it. The German military machine had, however, started to roll and it was now outwith the immediate control of its commander-in-chief, Wilhelm. The door to Armageddon was opening.

Across the English Channel, the British government too was becoming increasingly alarmed but continued to vacillate over the crisis in its efforts to remain detached from events on the continent, but by late July, it was clear that the situation was deteriorating by the hour. On 26th, Foreign Secretary Sir Edward Grey proposed that Britain, France, Germany and Italy meet to arbitrate the Austro-Hungarian dispute with Serbia. Chancellor von Bethmann-Hollweg rejected the proposal outright.

The following day, and by now probably too late for decisive action in any event, the British Cabinet still failed to provide strong leadership, leaving Grey to once more urge diplomacy. This time, though, possibly at the personal intervention of the Kaiser, von Bethmann-Hollweg wrote to Berchtold asking him to reconsider Grey's proposal for arbitration. Vienna did not reply until the following day, the 28th. When it did come, the letter simply stated that Grey's suggestion had been overtaken by events: earlier that morning, Austria had declared war on Serbia.

Two days later, Russia mobilised her forces, and on 1st August, Germany responded by declaring war on Russia, followed on 3rd August by a declaration of war on France. The Schlieffen Plan became reality and German forces crossed the Belgian border, violating her neutrality and attacking her troops. At 11 o'clock on the morning of Tuesday 4th August 1914, ostensibly in fulfilment of its 1839 treaty obligation to Belgium, Great Britain declared war on Germany. In reality, Britain went to war to avoid the defeat of France. A victorious Germany would have access to Channel ports for its navy and that was something that Britain could not countenance.

After the announcement of war by Prime Minister Herbert Asquith, Sir Edward Grey commented with tragic foresight, "The lamps are going out all over Europe. We shall never see them lit again in our time." The door to Armageddon had been thrown open, and for the 980th time since mankind had discovered how, he went to war.

My Royal Engineers insignia

Chapter Seven

" 'Well, I think I do,' said Mr Pond meekly. 'You see, I had to worry it out for myself. It really did arise from an excess of Prussian obedience. It also arose from an excess of another Prussian weakness: contempt.' "

The Three Horsemen of Apocalypse – taken from
The Paradoxes of Mr Pond – GK Chesterton

On the farm we greeted the news of war with disbelief. The growing crisis in Europe had been widely reported by the newspapers, but with Britain not rattling any sabres, we felt that whatever happened, it would not involve us. The British declaration of war on Germany changed all that because it automatically included Canada, and anyway, I was still a British subject.

As a British dominion, Canada was able to determine its own level of involvement in the war, but despite its pitifully small standing army of only 3,110 men, the government readily nailed its colours to the mast, and on 5th August, the Governor General declared that a state of war existed between Canada and Germany. In addition to the standing army, the country did have a militia but this was not mobilised. Instead, the government raised a completely new force, the Canadian Expeditionary Force. In just a few weeks, more than 32,000 men volunteered for the CEF.

I knew that for the time being I had to abandon my plans to have a farm in Canada and return to England to enlist before the winter arrived and I was unable to travel. Nevertheless, I could not simply leave Mr Edwards at that time of year with the harvest so close and when everyone was needed to get the crops in. I sought Gray's advice and decided that I would stay until the harvest was completed and then leave. Iwan was also intending to volunteer at the same time and had told his father so, although Al would have to stay on the farm.

I wrote and told my parents of my intentions and that I would see them as soon as I was able to arrange my passage. I had been in Canada for more than the two years specified in the assisted passage scheme which had brought me over in 1912 and so I was free to return if I wished. I was not greatly attracted to the idea of an infantry regiment, which in hindsight was just as well, but did feel that the Royal Engineers [the RE] would be ideal because of my telephone system knowledge.

With autumn and the harvest safely gathered in, the time to leave the farm approached too fast. I had applied to return to England very soon after war had been declared but had to wait until I was allocated a ship. The Canadian government had chartered thirty-three Atlantic liners to transport the CEF across to Britain and a few places were available on each ship for returning expats who were going home to volunteer. In mid September I was notified that I would once more sail, by coincidence, on the SS *Canada*. I packed my belongings into my carpet bag ready to return to the country I thought I had left forever less than three years earlier. In my pocket, in addition to my train ticket and passage indent, I carried a certificate of competence from the telephone company, which I would need when volunteering for the RE.

When the day came, it was very hard to leave the wonderful friends I had made. Everybody turned out that morning to wish me a safe journey, good luck in France and the hope that I would soon return to the farm. I thanked Mr Edwards for the opportunity he had given me and told Iwan that perhaps we might meet in France. He had to stay on at the farm a little longer but hoped to be able to join up the following year.

Just as he had first met me on that bitterly cold March evening in 1912, so Moon Wolf rode with me to the railway station that last morning. We tethered the horses and waited on the platform for the train. He was not a demonstrative man but told me that when I got to France to remember what he had taught me about hunting.

"The enemy is like the snake; he watches and waits for your mistake; then he strikes. Move like the wolf; keep your eyes and ears open and your head down; watch where you are putting your feet, and be careful, my friend."

I would recall his words many times over the next four years and have cause to thank him.

Finally, as the train approached, he turned to me and held my shoulder in his powerful grip. "Ontiatén:ro' ne ki. Ó:nen ki' wáhi. Skén:nen."

I reciprocated his thanks for friendship and added my gratitude for his teaching. Then, in returning his valediction, I added in my best Mohawk, "Skén:nen." Peace and serenity. He smiled and shook my hand. The train had come to a stop. I picked up my carpet bag, opened the carriage door and stepped inside. I turned again to say a final goodbye, but Moon Wolf had already gone as silently as he had appeared on that first night. I smiled to myself; I understood so much more about the First Nations than when I had arrived.

With a couple of changes, the train took me via Toronto and Ottawa to the port of Quebec, where the Canadian 1st Division was preparing to sail to England. I arrived on the night of 23rd/24th September with the rain beating down from the north-east in horizontal stair rods. The weather was so bad that special trains brought the troops the sixteen miles from their camp at Valcartier to the port instead of marching as planned. However, the artillery and transport wagons had no alternative than to use the road despite the appalling conditions. It was a taste of what was to come for them.

Leaving the shelter of the station, I stepped out into the driving rain in search of the shipping office, which I found after several wrong turns amongst the growing mass of guns, vehicles, horses and men. My passage papers were checked and I was told to find somewhere dry to wait but to keep checking in at the office until called. The entire embarkation of 1,424 officers, 29,197 men, 7,000 horses, guns, vehicles and wagons onto the thirty-three liners was completed in less than three days. This was an impressive accomplishment, although inevitably, the civilian expats were last to be taken on board each ship. After thirty-six hours of hanging around the cold, wet dockside, living on coffee, stew and fish, I was very glad to get below decks out of the incessant rain which had refused to ease.

The fleet assembled in Gaspé Bay to await their Royal Navy escorts, His Majesty's Ships *Charybdis*, *Diana*, *Eclipse*, *Glory*, *Suffolk*, and *Talbot*. The battlecruiser HMS *Queen Mary* would replace the *Suffolk* during the long, slow and uneventful journey. In the early light of Saturday 3rd October, the convoy, in three lines astern, eased out of the bay to go to war. Passing Avalon Peninsula, we were joined by the SS *Florizel*, a sealing ship which now carried the Newfoundland Regiment.

The troops were being posted to Wiltshire for training on Salisbury Plain but no-one seemed to know which British port we would arrive at as the whole convoy was shrouded in secrecy for its own protection. It seemed strange to be back on the *Canada* but although the crossing was a little rough at times, I was not troubled with seasickness. The Canadian troops welcomed into their company those of us who were returning home to volunteer and I soon met up with lads from Ontàrio who knew Aylmer and the Edwards'. Although the journey was slow, it was much more enjoyable and the general company was much better than on my previous sailing. The days passed pleasantly in a succession of impromptu entertainments and exchange of stories until we were off Land's End and sailing up the English Channel. Our final destination proved to be Plymouth, where, until we docked on the evening of Wednesday 14th, even the locals knew nothing of our arrival.

I said goodbye to my travelling companions and headed off to the railway station, where I managed to catch the Birmingham train. The railways were now under direct government control for the duration but that didn't help me catch a train home from Birmingham. By the time I arrived there, the last train to Shrewsbury had gone and so I settled down in the waiting room for the early morning 'milk' train. I was still wearing my Canadian hide clothes and drew a few strange looks, but as the night wore on and the air chilled, I was very glad of them. I had written home at the beginning of September to let my parents know that I would be arriving before the end of the year, but without a telephone in the house, I couldn't tell them that I had landed at Plymouth and they certainly would not have expected a telegram.

It was raining in England too and when I eventually arrived at Cressage station later that Thursday morning, it was as if I had never been away. I covered the half a mile to Jasmine Cottage in five minutes and when I stepped out of the rain and through the front door, my mother was where she always seemed to be, standing at the range cooking. My father and Herbert were at work. With a gasp of joy and surprise, my mother rushed to greet and hug me. She looked aghast at the clothes I wore but took the wet hide poncho and hung it up. All the smells of home came flooding back to me, not least the rabbit stew which was beginning to simmer on the range and the aroma of fresh bread in the oven.

My free passage and train fares had been on the understanding that I reported to the Head Postmaster at Shrewsbury GPO offices in St Mary's Street upon my return. So on the following Monday, I took the train into town and reported in. I already knew that the Royal Engineers were very particular about who they recruited because, no matter what rank an individual held, the work of the RE was skilled within a wide range of trades, from civil engineering, through railway construction, mining and tunnelling to the signals service, which until 1920 was part of the RE. Armed with my certificate of competence from Canada, I presented myself with a view to continuing my training as a Line Telegraphist before joining the RE.

There was no conscription at this stage of the war, that didn't happen until 2nd March 1916, but I explained that I had just arrived back from Ontario and that this was why I had returned. The postmaster had already been informed of my expected arrival, and with so many GPO staff already on their way to France, he was glad to have me. I started work at Shrewsbury exchange the following week and the GPO informed the RE that I had reported in, that my training would continue and that I would be available to the army as and when required. Thus my own immediate future was settled and I began to learn as much as I could about telephone equipment and air line installation.

The RE processed my application papers, and not long afterwards I was called to attend for my medical and educational assessment. The necessary requirements having been satisfied and the certificate from the Ontario telephone company duly examined and checked for authenticity, I was told to return to work and that I would be sent for in a few months. My name was put on the army reserve list of Post Office operators, a list which was first instituted before the South African War. The army simply could not process the numbers of men volunteering, and since the RE was a specialist service and the training period of necessity that much longer than normal, the throughput of men was that much slower.

The lovely summer of the year was followed by another mild winter of unremitting rain and recurring floods. When the spring finally came and the rain stopped, it would be recorded as the wettest winter anyone had known and it heralded several years of wet weather which had arrived just in time to coincide with the war. It would be another ninety-nine years before Britain and Western Europe experienced a wetter winter.

At the beginning, all the talk was that the war would be over by Christmas, but when Christmas came, it wasn't over; it never is. Instead it was literally bogged down on what had become the Western Front. The season of peace and goodwill to all mankind seemed a very hollow sentiment that year. It was not a celebration, although we were happy to be together again as a family, and even Lucy managed to get home for half a day on Boxing Day afternoon, which fell on a Saturday that year. On Christmas Day, we all went to church in the village, where the service was dominated by prayers for peace and for our servicemen at the Front, on the sea and, for the first time, in the air. My mother was typically strong because she knew that it would not be long before I would leave again and might possibly be followed by Herbert, who was now sixteen.

Not since the Middle Ages, where laying siege to towns and castles was a common feature of medieval warfare, had armies planned a static war as a central plank of their strategy. The later development of weaponry and tactics had led generals to formulate plans on the premise that their armies would keep moving forward and their foe would keep moving backwards; a highly mobile war. General Schlieffen had been no exception and his plan, like so many plans before and since, calculated that the war would be over by Christmas. And so it was, but not that first Christmas; there would be another three before it was all over.

There was no-one who really envisaged what was happening in Europe. Governments did not believe that the European powers were so evenly matched that a stalemate would ensue; financially, it was believed that no nation could withstand the economic burden of a protracted stationary war, and military strategists had no plan for it. Each side calculated, as did Schlieffen, that men and cavalry would move swiftly through their opposing forces and reach their objectives in a short time. Perversely, there was only a small window of historical opportunity for this war to develop as it did. Thirty years sooner, it would probably not have been logistically, economically and technologically possible; twenty years later, it was an outdated form overtaken by blitzkrieg and air power, which is really what Schlieffen had planned but his successors had been unable to deliver it.

When war broke out, because of compulsory military service in peacetime, Germany's standing army was raised from 791,000 to five million men in a few days; Austria-Hungary's from 450,000 to 3,350,000; France's 790,000 to four million and Russia's from 1,200,000 to six million men. Britain had a mere 160,000 men and although there was a territorial force, it was pitifully inadequately equipped and largely untrained for front-line fighting duties, as most of its volunteers had signed up for general Home duties only. It was largely what the Home Guard was to be some years later.

Perhaps unsurprisingly, even the perpetually neutral Belgians had a larger army than Britain, albeit not as well trained, but that did not prevent it fighting as hard and determinedly as any force in the coming war. Germany, which had been preparing for this for many years, ensured that its infantry were well equipped and issued them with the robust and accurate Mauser rifle. It also far out-gunned all other nations in all categories of artillery and weaponry on land, and in particular in its understanding of the strategic battlefield use of the machine gun, an awareness which the British military hierarchy woefully lacked at this time.

German patrols had started to cross into France before the formal declaration of war. One such incursion was at Belfort at 09.59 on the morning of 2nd August, when Corporal Jules-André Peugeot and his three colleagues challenged a German cavalry patrol which had entered the town, telling them that they were under arrest. The officer leading the patrol was Leutnant Albert Otto Walter Mayer of the 29th Cavalry Brigade, who, seeing Peugeot barring his way, shot him. Despite being hit in the shoulder, Peugeot returned fire but missed. The two patrols exchanged fire and Mayer was hit in the stomach and head. The leutnant grunted, slumped forward in his saddle, then fell to the ground, dead. His patrol retreated. Corporal Peugeot was helped back to their billet house, where he died at 10.37. They were the first Imperial German Army and French Army soldiers to die in the Great War.

In the twenty days following 15th July, German efficiency and their railway system transported 3,100,000 men in 11,000 trains across the Rhine at Cologne ready for the assault. Then, just before dawn broke on 4th August, the Kaiser's troops commanded by General Otto von Emmich crossed the border into Belgium. Civilians stood in front of their homes and watched in silent helplessness as seemingly endless ranks of invading soldiers and cavalry filled the dusty roads of this neutral nation, marching onwards for hour after hour until nightfall. The following day it was the same until it seemed that all of Germany was trampling over Belgian soil heading for the Meuse River near Visé and the bridge crossing there. War in Europe was always about bridges and ridges.

The Belgian Army was deployed further south defending Liège, the gateway to France. Sniper fire from the defenders of Visé and elsewhere was countered by the summary execution of civilians or the complete destruction of villages. Nothing could be permitted to impede the progress of the marching army, for speed was essential if France was to be conquered before it could mobilise and deploy its huge army effectively and before the British arrived. However, when von Emmich's two cavalry divisions and six infantry brigades reached the bridge over the Meuse, they found that it had been blown, and so started a catalogue of delays which prevented the Germans from capturing Liège with the ease that had been anticipated and planned. Unable to surmount its ring of concrete forts, on 6th August, the army commander ordered an aerial attack. Zeppelin ZVI flew over the city and dropped thirteen bombs, killing nine civilians.

The raid in itself had no impact upon the defences or the battle but it was significant in its own right. It was the first known dedicated bombing raid from the air in history, thus both fulfilling and vindicating the vision and scientific faith of Jesuit mathematician and aeronautics pioneer, Father Francesco Lana de Terzi. In his book *Prodromo*, published in 1670, de Terzi explained his concept and calculations for a 'flying ship' and how it would work. Often described as 'the father of aeronautics', he also recognised the capabilities of his design as a weapon of war with which to attack cities from the air.

The designer believed that his idea would, though, remain theory, and wrote with some regret, "*God will never allow man to construct such a machine, since it would create many disturbances in the civil and political governments of mankind. Where is the man who can fail to see that no city would be proof against surprise, when the ship could at any time be steered over its squares, or even over the courtyards of dwelling-houses, and brought to earth for the landing of its crew?...Iron weights could be hurled to wreck ships at sea, or they could be set on fire by fireballs and bombs; nor ships alone, but houses, fortresses and cities could be thus destroyed, with the certainty that the airship could come to no harm as the missiles could be hurled from a vast height.*" Whatever else was within de Terzi's contemplation at the time he was writing, the extent of his fellow man's appetite for killing each other three centuries later was not included.

The 165,000 men of the Belgian Army, led by General Gérard Leman, had fought with a courage, tenacity and commitment which no-one had expected, least of all the German Imperial General Staff. The war had only just begun and already Schlieffen's plan was four to five days behind schedule. The effect of the Belgians' stalwart defence of their country would go far beyond the first week of the war; it would shape the whole conflict. The slowed advance through Belgium allowed time for the French and the British to deploy their forces to meet the invader. The

British had to ship everything across the English Channel, and since Britain's involvement in the war had been rather last minute, there had not been the opportunity to have a prolonged build-up, and so these few days were critical to the Allies and would ultimately prove fatal to the success of the invasion. Germany would have to wait another twenty-six years to realise its ambition.

The fighting men of the British Expeditionary Force were relatively easy to ferry across to France, but with them needed to go food, ammunition, artillery, transport vehicles, horses to pull the transport and the guns, fodder for the horses, field ambulances, hospitals, vets, doctors, nurses, farriers, blacksmiths, wheelwrights, cookhouses, and so on and so forth, including the Royal Engineers and all their various specialist equipment, particularly the communication equipment, albeit fairly primitive. It all took time.

The Zeppelin attack on Liège heralded the birth of a whole new dimension of fighting; aerial warfare had arrived and both the British government and the Chiefs of Staff had been slow to recognise the military value of the aeroplane, seeing it only as an observation platform. Britain was lagging a long way behind its foe. On 8th August, whilst the Belgians continued to defy German expectations, the fledgling Royal Flying Corps, only formed in May 1912 from the Air Battalion of the Royal Engineers, under the command of Brigadier-General Sir David Henderson, gathered together what equipment it could and rendezvoused at Dover. For the next five days, the ground crews arrived with their newly requisitioned maintenance vehicles: a bright red 'Bovril' van, another advertising 'Stephens' Blue-Black Ink', a third emblazoned with 'Lazenby's Sauce [the World's Appetiser]' and the fourth promoting the culinary delights of 'Peek-Frean's Biscuits'.

13th August heralded the arrival of the aircraft: some AV 504 single-seat fighters made by AV Roe & Co, several of Geoffrey de Havilland's BE2s, eight BE8s, and a handful of painfully slow

Henri Farmans. Some of these aircraft looked alarmingly frail, particularly the Farmans, which we had recently bought from the French because they no longer had any use for them. This whole event had a carnival atmosphere for the people of Dover who had turned out to see the aircraft arrive, and was something of an entertainment not unlike the arrival of Louis Blériot's little monoplane only five years earlier, when he also landed at Dover after his historic first aeroplane crossing of the English Channel.

The thirty-seven pilots of Nos.2, 3, 4 and 5 Squadrons gathered for an evening meal followed by a restless night as each one considered the first hurdle which the following day held; the flight across the English Channel. On Friday 14th August, Lt. HD Harvey-Kelly of No.2 Squadron was the first RFC pilot to land in France during the Great War. Many years into the future, for wars of a very different kind, AV Roe and Geoffrey de Havilland would, between them, go on to produce three of the world's most iconic bombers, the Mosquito, the Lancaster, and the Vulcan.

Early August belonged to Germany. Having eventually suppressed Liège, the right wing of the invading forces bypassed Brussels and moved south-westwards with apparent ease until reaching Mons, where the BEF held them for the two days of 22nd - 23rd. Despite Germany's preparedness, the well-equipped men of the BEF were probably the most highly trained troops and best infantry marksmen in the world. Nevertheless, outnumbered and out-gunned, they were forced to retreat and fight a series of rearguard actions on the way. It was at Mons that Corporal E Thomas of the 4th Irish Dragoon Guards fired the first British shot of the war. The battle also produced the first Victoria Crosses of the war, to Lieutenant Maurice Dease and Private Sidney Godley. With most of his section dead or injured, Lieutenant Dease, already wounded five times and bleeding heavily, manned the machine gun and held up the German advance. When he passed out, the gun was taken over by Private Godley until his position was overrun and he was captured.

Amongst those that were left behind at Mons was John Henry Parr from Finchley, accepted as the first British soldier to be killed in the Great War, although the circumstances of his death are uncertain. Like so many after him, Parr had lied about his age, telling the recruitment officer that he was seventeen; he was actually fourteen. He is buried, as is Lt. Dease VC, at St. Symphorien cemetery and lies, by complete chance though separated by four years of war, opposite George Edwin Ellison, killed at 9.30am on 11th November 1918, the last British soldier to die in the conflict. Ellison, who also fought at the First Battle of Mons, would go on to see action in the First Battle of Ypres, then at Armentières, La Bassée, Lens, Loos and Cambrai. He would return to Mons in the final days of the war as British forces retook the ground lost in 1914, only to be killed whilst on patrol ninety minutes before the Armistice took effect.

Having failed to hold the German advance, the British pulled back to join the French on the south bank of the River Marne as part of the defence of Paris. General Moltke and his staff were now so convinced of victory that it had not entered their calculations that these were prepared defensive positions, believing their enemies to be in complete rout. Germany's rapid progress across the battlefield created a substantial problem of poor communication between its headquarters staff and the forward commanders. With distance, the field telephone lines became increasingly unreliable until eventually all contact was lost. Vital intelligence information failed to be passed on to field commanders, who were left to guess where they were in relation to the British and French forces.

Approaching Paris but still north of the Marne, the First and Second Armies commanded by Generals Kluck and Bülow were becoming exhausted. Out on the right wing of the great revolving attacking wheel, they had to move faster than the inner left wing to keep the line of the battle plan. It was here that the impact of Moltke's earlier decision to weaken the right wing and strengthen the left wing began to undermine Schlieffen's strategy. Without sufficient resources to pass around Paris to the west, Kluck and Bülow were forced to turn in and close on Paris from the east.

Caught out of position and lacking intelligence reports, Kluck was vulnerable to simultaneous attack from front and rear. Had the British Expeditionary Force Commander-in-Chief Field Marshal Sir John French heeded the request of his highly experienced ally, General Gallieni, and moved his troops forward quickly into the gap between Kluck's and Bülow's forces, Kluck would have been soundly defeated at the Marne. At that point, the war might well then have taken a very different turn as the French forts at Epinal, Toul and Verdun had decimated the attacking forces from the east and halted the German advance of the left wing, depriving Kluck of rescue.

As it was, a combination of Sir John French's unnecessarily over-cautious rate of advance and the decision-making pedantry of France's supreme commander, General Joffre, allowed the Imperial Army to withdraw to previously selected positions along the north bank of the River Aisne and dig in. The British and French troops did likewise and trench warfare began. There then followed a race to the sea as each side sought to out-flank the other. It only ended when the North Sea coast was reached and the Belgians opened the sea defence gates to flood the low lying land of the Yser region near Nieuwpoort. By the end of the year, the Front stretched for 475 miles from the North Sea to the Swiss border. As news of the stalemate in France and Belgium reached Britain, and with the realisation that, as Secretary of State for War Lord Kitchener had predicted, the war would not be over by Christmas, it was hardly surprising that up and down the country in homes of rich and poor alike, instead of festive cheer, there was serious discussion and contemplation about what the following year would hold. Churches across the land were fuller than usual as people prayed for both victory and peace. Cressage was no exception, and I have no doubt that in the churches of our enemies, the congregations were offering up the same prayers.

For many young men across the spectrum of backgrounds, the chance to enlist in Kitchener's Army at the outbreak of war was greeted with great enthusiasm. That enthusiasm was motivated by anything from raw patriotism, through a youthful thirst for excitement to an escape from the daily drudgery of office or factory work or from the misery of unemployment, hunger and poverty. Men of all ages, many claiming to be older than they were, others younger, answered Kitchener's call for a New Army in their tens of thousands. They were universally referred to as 'Kitchener's Mob', but would experience the attrition of the trenches and the carnage of the Western Front and Gallipoli, where they would pay an appalling price in lost or broken lives and suffering. Some would instead see action in Greece and the Mediterranean, Mesopotamia, Arabia and Africa, but most would bear the pain of separation from home and family for even longer than their comrades in France and Belgium. For many, the time would prove too long and the wife or sweetheart they had left at home would not be waiting upon their return.

Inevitably, young lads from the same district or few streets were encouraged to volunteer together and were formed into battalions from those areas, becoming known as the 'Pals Battalions', of which the Accrington Pals would perhaps become the best known. However, it was not just the ties of neighbourhoods that produced volunteers for Pals Battalions, but men from similar professions, trades, jobs and interests, including city stockbrokers, solicitors, public schools, professional sports clubs, football in particular, and social backgrounds, all rushed to take the King's Shilling. The 16th (2nd Edinburgh) (Service) Battalion, Royal Scots contained the entire Heart of Midlothian Football Club first and reserve team players, several boardroom and staff members and a large contingent of its supporters. In all, the Pals Battalions accounted for 145 Service and seventy Reserve units, over twenty percent of the battalions raised in the first two years of war.

Iwan outside the farmhouse with his parents and three brothers just before he left to go to war

Our friend Joe with his sisters also ready to go to France

Chapter Eight

" The Queen she sent to look for me,
The sergeant he did say,
'Young man, a soldier will you be
For thirteen pence a day?"'
Grenadier – AE Housman

It was nice to be home, especially for my mother's cooking, but I had changed whilst I had been away. Everything around me seemed strangely small and close at hand after the vastness of Ontario. I also missed the companionship of the people and friends that I had worked with although I was made very welcome at the Shrewsbury exchange. Inevitably, though, at a time when generally people did not travel far and few went overseas, they all wanted to hear about my time in Canada.

I was officially apprenticed for the present and the GPO were trying to teach me as much as possible in as short a time as possible and thus I would go out with the skilled linemen and engineers. I was quickly transferred to the Much Wenlock depot, which saved me taking the train into Shrewsbury every day. One morning in mid April, the jobs list included a visit to Littlecote, the home of Lady Harnage. Whilst we were working upon the fault, her Ladyship came into the room to see how we were getting along. She was now very elderly and wasn't always well enough to attend church, especially during the winter, but she had seen me there a couple of times and so knew that I had returned from Canada to enlist. This, however, was the first time that we had spoken beyond the courtesies of a Sunday greeting, and before we left, she asked me to call and see her the following Sunday afternoon if I was not doing anything. I wasn't, but even if I had been, it would have had to be something very important to turn down her invitation.

I duly presented myself at Littlecote at 3 o'clock and was shown into the morning room by a very pretty maid of about eighteen, who was wearing a fitted grey pinafore dress and starched white linen apron and cap. I recognised her from around the village and attending church with her employer, but didn't know her name. Telling me that her Ladyship would be with me presently, the maid asked me to sit down and then withdrew. She was such a breath of fresh air compared to her predecessor.

A few minutes later I stood up again as Lady Harnage entered the room. I hadn't really noticed earlier in the week, but she seemed now to be much older than when I had come to say goodbye to her before leaving for Canada, even though it had been barely three years ago. Now in her advanced years, the outbreak of the war, with no early end in sight, troubled her deeply. She was, though, as graceful as ever. There was no air of superiority about her for she cared deeply about the village and its people and she knew that Cressage would lose some of its sons before the war was over.

She sat down, straight-backed as always, and beckoned me to my chair. I was one at the same time a grown man and yet still one of her boys. It was the man before her who was extended the privilege of afternoon tea brought in and served by that pretty young maid. I looked at her and smiled; she blushed, and because she was in her mistress's presence, looked away quickly and, after serving the tea, left the room. Elizabeth Harnage did not miss my smile or her maid's blush. She looked at me knowingly, and now it was my turn to blush. But that was not why I was there.

How was Canada? How long was the journey there and what was it like? Where did I go, what did I do, what did I see and learn? What were the people like? How did I get back? She wanted to know all about it and was genuinely interested to hear of my experiences. It was the boy who now sat before her and for the next hour I regaled her with tales of a distant and exciting land, of the First Nation peoples, of great storms at sea and on land, of fields of grain that stretched as far as the eye could see, of the vast expanses of lakes and forests, of the wolves, the Northern Lights and the splendorous wonders of nature on a scale unimaginable in Britain.

She was enthralled and her eyes sparkled as she imagined the scenes I described, but presently she began to look tired and I knew that it was time to take my leave. I rose from my seat as she rang for her maid.

"Violet is not spoken for, Rowland." She looked at me and the faintest of smiles creased the corners of her elderly but still delicate mouth.

The door opened as Violet came to show me out and I thanked her Ladyship for having me. It would be the last time that I saw Elizabeth Harnage; a true lady in every sense, who had helped and encouraged me and many other Cressage children through their childhood.

At the outside door, I told Violet my name, where I lived and asked her if she would accompany me to the forthcoming Mayday celebrations, being held as usual despite the war.

"Yes, I know who you are and where you live," she said. "I know your sister Lucy, so I'll think about it and send a message with her."

About a week later, Lucy came home one evening to visit Mother, who had been unwell. The late April sunshine was still warm and I was helping my father plant runner bean seeds in the garden when Lucy strolled up and casually said, "Well, you're a dark horse, Rowland. I didn't know that you knew the lovely Violet Davies."

"I don't really," I mumbled, staying bent over to hide my reddening face from my sister.

"Well, I have a message for you from her anyway. She says that you may take her to the Maypole dance on Saturday. You're to call for her at 2 o'clock."

Saturday 1ˢᵗ May 1915 was, just as I remembered Maydays from my childhood, a lovely bright sunny day. Although a little cloud bubbled up in the afternoon, the day stayed fine, dry and pleasantly warm. Lady Harnage was no longer well enough to attend the event but the school children still wore gaily coloured smocks and danced around the maypole as the music played and rang in our ears. The troubles of Europe seemed a long way off and it was as if I had never been away. I had missed all this in Canada. It was, though, the beginning of the final act of the rapidly fading world into which I had been born. Soon, nothing would be as it was ever again; the England of old was already being swept away.

I really enjoyed my day with Violet, but as the dusk began to gather, it was time to walk her back to Littlecote. We arranged to meet again, but when the day came, she was unable to see me as Lady Harnage was unwell and needed her. I did see Violet briefly in church at morning service on the following Sundays, but we were not able to speak other than a formal greeting.

A further opportunity to see her did not present itself because, on Friday 29ᵗʰ May, I received notification that I was to report to Shrewsbury on 8ᵗʰ June to swear my attestation, from where I would go directly to commence my military service. It was time to leave home again.

That morning upon attestation, I held the Holy Bible in my right hand, which I then raised and swore, "*by Almighty God that I will bear true Allegiance to His Majesty King George the Fifth, His Heirs and*

Successors, and I will, as in duty bound, honestly and faithfully defend His Majesty, His Heirs and Successors, in Person, Crown and dignity against all enemies and will observe and obey all orders of His Majesty, His Heirs and Successors and of the Generals and Officers set over me. So help me God."

And that was that; I was now no longer Mr Rowland Hill but Sapper Hill, number 75780, Telegraphist Royal Engineers. The Corps of Royal Engineers can trace its history all the way back to 1066 and William the Conqueror and can claim 950 years of unbroken service to the Crown. Members of the RE have served the Crown in many different ways over the years, including work as architects and designers of buildings as disparate as the Royal Albert Hall and, at a cost of £84,186-12s-2d, Pentonville jail.

In 1911, the RE had formed its Air Battalion and in doing so created the first flying unit of the British armed services, and it was the forerunner of the Royal Flying Corps and, later, the Royal Air Force. The RE have no battle honours; instead their mottos, *Ubique* [Everywhere] and *Quo Fas Et Gloria Ducunt* [Where Duty and Glory Lead], granted by William IV in 1832 are evidence that they have served in every major combat arena and most minor ones. William IV simultaneously granted the same mottos to the Royal Artillery for the same reasons.

My travel warrant to Bletchley in Buckinghamshire was tucked safely into my wallet together with a copy of my enlistment letter dated 28th May under Army Order 296 and 341, signed by Colonel AM Ogilvie, Director of Army Signals, Home Defence. I made my way to Shrewsbury station where I waited with several other new recruits to the army for the Birmingham train. I was on the way to my first posting and my initial training at the RE Signal Depot at Staple Hall, Fenny Stratford.

This pleasant country house and open grounds was owned by Sir Herbert and Lady Leon, who also owned Bletchley Park, which lay just across the railway tracks from the Hall. Within a fortnight of war being declared, Staple Hall had been requisitioned by the army as accommodation for 2,000 territorials, and 16th August saw the arrival of these troops. At that stage, the Hall was used as the officers' mess, with other ranks billeted in houses around Fenny Stratford and Bletchley. Additionally, the Hall also provided stabling for a hundred horses.

Whatever contingency plans for war that Britain might have had, they did not extend to this level of detail, and with the rapid movement of troops and volunteers, accommodation was a serious problem. The billeting of other ranks in private houses was seen as a short-term expediency and as such it was not always handled with the care and foresight that might have proved prudent. On one occasion, an incredibly naïve, insensitive or simply over-stretched billeting officer took the decision to place ten soldiers in a house occupied by a mother and her three teenage daughters, living there on their own. It was then hardly surprisingly that, before too long, all four women found that they were pregnant, and the absence of any recorded criminal or military charges would suggest that the women were entirely compliant with the activities which led to their own predicament.

No doubt, and much to the relief of at least a part of the local population, by 22nd January 1915, the territorials began to move out and were replaced by the Royal Engineers who were to set up the Signal Training School. By February, 800 men and a different one hundred horses were installed. This time, though, there were no billets in private houses. When I arrived there in June, other ranks were accommodated in tents set up in the grounds of the Hall. These would be our quarters for the foreseeable future.

The International Stores building at the corner of George Street and Aylesbury Street was taken over and used as a Soldiers' Institute where we could go to get away from our training camp, buy a cup of tea and a bun, and sit quietly to read in one room or play games and chat in another. In the winter we played football at Staple Hall, but during the summer months Sir Herbert gave us permission to play cricket on the splendid sports field at Bletchley Park, which, twenty-five years later would come to hold a very special place in the history of Britain's defence during the next war with Germany.

The train from Shrewsbury took me to Birmingham, where I had to change for Bletchley. I arrived in the late-afternoon sunshine and, since the station is very close to Staple Hall, it only took me a few minutes to walk there. I was feeling quite excited and looking forward to the start of my training, but then I had no idea really of what awaited me. I showed my letter to the sentry on the gate to the Hall grounds. He directed me into the guardhouse, where I reported and again showed my letter. The duty corporal checked my name against a list and then gave me the number of the tent in which I would be sleeping. These were all bell tents which slept ten men in a circle, feet towards the central pole and were arranged in rows within part of the open grounds of the Hall. I soon found the right tent and introduced myself to the two young lads who were already established in it, having arrived the day before.

They told me what little they knew of the camp routine so far as I began to unpack my faithful, well-travelled carpet bag. The first thing I noticed was that there were no beds. To keep us off the damp ground, each man had a board not unlike a door to sleep on but with no mattress or 'biscuits', no sheets and no pillow, just three blankets. I folded two blankets over the boards to give me some slight cushion and the third one I kept to cover myself with. It was June in England and warm; not long ago I had been living through Canadian winters so the cool of the Buckinghamshire night-time air would not trouble me.

It seemed that nothing much was going to happen until all the new recruits had arrived during the course of the week. However, each day, such uniforms and kit that were available were issued to those who had arrived and I collected mine from the store the following morning. The uniform was neither made to measure nor anything like new. Nothing really matched, but what I found most disturbing was that the jacket had a bullet hole just below the right-hand breast pocket and the faded stains of what had clearly been the blood of the previous wearer which the cleaners had been unable to remove. When I pointed this out to the storeman, he just laughed and said to think myself lucky I wasn't wearing it at the time and to go and sew it up!

Most of what was itemised on the army kit list I had been handed was missing. I was told that these items would be issued as my training progressed, along with a new uniform. The basic kit I did get included:

1 × book, pay, soldier for use, AB64
1 × disc, identity
1 × jacket, Service Dress [SD]
1 × trousers, Service Dress
1 × braces, pair, trousers Service Dress for use with
1 × puttees, pair
1 × cap, Service Dress
1 × badge, cap
1 × boots, leather, black, pair, mounted for, B5 type
1 × holdall, equipped, infantry issue
1 × knife, clasp, infantry issue
1 × tin, mess, set, infantry issue

And so it went on. A shirt, vest and pants, RE shoulder insignia, several training manuals, various brushes for cleaning boots and uniform, polish, and a kitbag to put it all in were included in the raw recruits' basic issue. The holdall contained a knife, fork and spoon, spare boot laces, button brass, toothbrush, shaving brush and cut-throat razor. Whilst I had been in Canada, I had bought a Gillette safety razor, so I never used my cut-throat for shaving, although I did use it for a variety of other non-King's Regulations purposes. The soldier's Pay Book, AB64 [Army Book 64], which replaced the Soldiers' Small Book, Army Form 50, was the most important document we carried. It was in effect an instruction guide for new recruits containing everything from the rules about saluting officers, how to do it, when to do it and for how long to hold the salute to a page for making a Will, which was a mandatory requirement for all troops sent to the Front.

The first job when I got back to my tent was to sort out all this stuff, decide how much of what I had brought with me I would keep, and then mark everything with my name and army number, 75780, which had already been stamped onto my identity disc by the storeman. These discs were universally known as dog tags or, with the soldier's usual sardonic sense of humour, the 'cold meat ticket'.

That done, I set about mending the bullet hole with my own mending kit which I had put together in Canada. Edwards's farm had been somewhat isolated and so we had needed to be self-sufficient in many ways and especially when it came to repairing clothes and equipment in the winter time. During the long evenings of my first winter there, Moon Wolf had taught me how to sew like a Mohawk; the careful intricate stitches that will never come undone unless you unpick them. As I carefully stitched the hole, I quickly realised that the skills I had learned would stand me in good stead in the army. The two lads in the tent with me were fascinated to watch me sewing up the bullet hole with the strong green thread in a way they had never witnessed their mothers doing, and they wanted to know how and where I had learned the technique; and then of course they wanted to hear all about Canada. I was happy to share some of my adventures with them.

It helped to pass the time, to take their minds off the homesickness caused by being away from home for the first time and create a bond with people I would serve with and probably have to fight with.

Finally, the patch was complete and almost invisible. Satisfied that it would outlast the rest of the jacket, I shed my civilian clothes and tried on the various parts of my uniform. Nothing fitted. The jacket was too tight, the trousers were too long and the sleeves of the shirt had come from a different shirt than the body. With much reluctance, I put all my civvies into the carpet bag, tied it up with string, filled out the label with my parents' address and handed it in. Later that day, the duty driver loaded my bag with several others onto a handcart and took it round to the parcel office at the nearby Fenny Stratford station. Two days later, the old porter at Cressage station unloaded my trusty bag from the goods wagon and persuaded one of the young boys from the village to deliver my bag to Jasmine Cottage to save himself the walk. He gave the boy tuppence and told him that Mrs Hill might give him another tuppence if he was quick and went straight there. He did, and received the promised pennies from my mother; my belongings were safely home. It would be some years before I would need them again.

The Service Dress jacket and trousers were made of wool serge, which, although warm, was rough and itchy at first. The jacket had no belt, was designed to be worn loose fitting and buttoned to the top as we wore no tie, although mine was so tight I could hardly breathe. There were five King's crown buttons down the front. The RE was a mounted service and so in time I was also issued with a pair of riding breeches which laced over my calves. When not riding, I wore my SD trousers with puttees, a long woollen serge ribbon about 2 inches wide and wound around the calves between the bottom of the knee and the ankle over the boot. The idea, which was very effective, was to give support and keep stones, grit and other unwanted items from dropping into the boots and causing foot damage when marching. I soon learned that, as a mounted Service, we wound our puttees from the knee to the ankle instead of the other way; a little trait which immediately distinguished mounted troops, including the RE and artillery, from all other troops, especially the infantry. The reason was to stop the puttees coming undone at the knee from friction against the saddle if breeches were not worn.

I bought some dubbin at the ironmongers in Fenny Stratford and spent most of that first week soaking my boots with it to waterproof and soften them, and learning to tie my puttees properly. The trick was to start at exactly the right place just below the knee and then wind them around leaving exactly the same distance of about an inch between each lap whilst still ending up with the tapes in the right place to tie off around the ankle. It took some practice, but I soon got the hang of it, and after a few days could do it very quickly.

There was a training corporal in charge of the men in each group of three tents. Our corporal was a decent sort of chap and had been in the regular army for nearly thirty years, long enough to have seen action in South Africa during the Boer War of 1899–1902. We came to know him as strict in discipline, fair in judgment, deep in knowledge and experience. It was his job to teach us the basics of soldiering, physical training, drill, and musketry. When we asked him where our guns were, he laughed and told us that we would not be trusted with a gun until we had learned to be soldiers first.

By the end of the week, there were about two hundred new recruits. Staple Hall Camp housed around 800 men; some were on the permanent training staff, others, like me, were going through at different stages of their training regime. Each day started at 6am, when the raucous hooter which the RE had installed when they

137

arrived at the Hall in January intruded into peaceful slumber, rousing not only the soldiers in the camp but many of the good people of Fenny Stratford and Bletchley as well, much to their enduring irritation.

That really set the scene for the first six weeks of our training, for it had nothing to do with telephones and everything to do with learning to be soldiers. When the hooter sounded, we got up, tidied the tent, had a brew and then, dressed in shorts and singlet PT kit, did physical exercise for half an hour whilst the duty corporal bawled instructions at us for running on the spot, burpees, press-ups, legs and arms akimbo, touching toes, etc.

Afterwards, we went to the ablution area to have a wash and a shave and then collected our breakfast, which was usually porridge followed by sausages, bread and cheese. This was followed by drill. Learning to march and drilling had two main purposes; firstly, it helped with fitness and got us used to working in our uniforms. Secondly, and much more importantly, it got us used to taking orders. Drilling constantly, turning this way and that, stopping and starting as a body of men on the word of a command had the effect of teaching us to respond to an order immediately without stopping to think about what we had been ordered to do. On the battlefield, this is essential. You cannot fight effectively if every order that is given is thought about and questioned by the person receiving it.

Drill lasted until lunchtime at 12.15, when we had a good lunch, usually of stew and potatoes and a chance to remove our boots and ease aching feet. We resumed again at 2pm until 4.30pm. After that, we were free to do as we wished, although in practice that meant cleaning the tent, our uniforms and polishing our boots, or bulling them, as it was known. At 6pm, tea was dished up and then we were free again. For two weeks, this was our daily routine without alteration. At the end of this time, we were definitely a lot fitter and beginning to feel like soldiers.

After that, some variation was introduced to the routine; instead of drilling in the afternoon, we were marched to an area of the grounds furthest from the house, given a shovel and told to dig trenches. Each afternoon for a week we dug trenches and then we filled them in again! We were then introduced to the joys of route marches, which were usually between twenty and twenty-five miles. With full kit on and carrying about fifty pounds on our backs, we marched around the Buckinghamshire countryside at about three miles per hour, with short breaks; the breaks usually being determined by the smoking needs of the drill serjeant or his assessment of our performance. There was no band to accompany us but we were allowed to sing the songs of the day to help us keep in step and to keep the pace going. Inevitably, there were those amongst us who knew some alternative words to many of the tunes, but we had to be careful when marching through villages to sing the correct words so as not to cause offence to local women who often came out to watch us go by.

Our kit was gradually topped up and replaced piecemeal as we went through our training, more or less being given what we would need at the time we needed it and not before, although we did spend the first two weeks doing PT in our underwear and boots since no singlets and shorts were yet available to us.

By the end of July and after six weeks' hard training, we were very fit and some of the young lads from poorer homes had even started to fill out and put on some weight; the benefit, and for some of them the novelty, of having three good meals every day. From then on, our training became more varied and the day came that we were taken to the stables. It was an essential skill at this time for RE officers and men to be competent riders, for once in France, the horse would be part of our transport behind the lines. Although the heavier equipment and cable in particular would be on motorised transport, horses still provided a quick and useful form of transport and would often work pulling the transport carts in conditions where vehicles could not manage.

We were split into groups of twenty, but before being allocated a horse, we were instructed in the basic physiology of the animal and also in its care. The army was very careful with its horses as they were considered to be much more valuable than a soldier. They certainly cost a great deal more to keep than a soldier, since at that stage of our training, all we earned was a shilling a day – just tuppence more than I had been paid for a single hour's work in Canada.

In due course, we were each handed the reins of a saddled horse. Having shown us how to get onto a horse, the serjeant instructor told us to mount up. There were about half a dozen of us who rode, and so before we did so we checked that the saddle was properly secured to the horse. Intuitively we knew that it wouldn't be, and we each started to adjust the straps around the horse's middle, but before we got very far, there were shouts and cries from those not familiar with horses who had tried to get on and simply slid off, saddle and all. Lesson number one, always check the saddle straps. However, serjeant instructors do not like recruits who know too much.

Recognising that this small group knew at least something about riding, he separated the six of us and then said that since we were so smart one of us would volunteer to ride around the course to show the others how easily it could be done. The intention to reassert his authority and have some fun at our expense was clear enough. Although the serjeant did not know it, the others all knew that I had been to Canada and had done a lot of riding, so I volunteered to do the ride. With a sly smile of anticipation at the forthcoming disaster, the serjeant then played his trump card and told me to remove the saddle of my mount, get on and gallop around the course, including the jumps, which were not so much fences as low training jumps.

I not only knew how to sew like a Mohawk but also how to ride like one too. I threw my cap to one of the lads and, with rising spirits, set off round the course, for all the world wishing I was back on the prairies. I could feel the power of the animal beneath me and the pleasure of riding again surged through my veins as we galloped around the field without any trouble at all. In fact, the horse I had been given was a very nice animal, well trained and extremely easy to handle.

Ten minutes later, we raced up to where the serjeant was standing and, in a flurry of flying earth, came to a stop, forcing him to step back away from the horse. I knew that it was a big mistake, but it had been the most enjoyable ten minutes since I had arrived at Staple Hall. All the lads were cheering and clapping, until the serjeant barked an order and silence fell over the group. He told me that since there was clearly nothing that he could teach me about riding, I would be wasting my time for the rest of the afternoon so I would be of better use peeling potatoes. And that is what I did every afternoon for three days; the punishment was supposedly for riding whilst improperly dressed with no cap, but everyone knew that it was for denying him the delight of seeing me sprawled across the field with my horse back at the stable. After that though, he did enlist my help in teaching those who were less familiar with and less comfortable around horses; honour and authority had been re-established.

Some few days later, one of the officers stopped me and said that he had seen the incident at the riding course and asked where I had learned to ride like that. I told that I had grown up with horses at home and on the farm, but had been taught to ride bareback by a Mohawk warrior in Canada. He was very interested and said he knew where to come if they needed someone for the polo team, but of course I didn't get to play polo.

The next stage of training was musketry and bayonet fighting practice, but since we had been using wooden replica rifles to drill with, I wasn't sure what they had in mind. All the best rifles were needed for the troops at the Front and at this stage of the war, there were not enough spare for training use. Consequently, it was old Boer War MLE rifles that we were issued with. In its day, the Magazine Lee Enfield had been a very good weapon but it had been superseded by the SMLE, the Short Magazine Lee Enfield for front-line troops.

Some of the trenches dug by the intake after us were deliberately left open and we used these to practise trench warfare. Half the group got down into the trench as defenders whilst the other half acted as attackers. The corporal in charge showed us how to parry a lunge and also how to avoid the parry. This was all well and good until a few got carried away and really thought that those of us in the trench were the enemy. It was a close call, with some bayonets almost skewering their targets.

We also practised bayonet charges on straw-filled dummies hung up from a sort or gantry and made to look like a German soldier. Demonstrating an unhealthy timidity, with fixed bayonets, we ran at the dummies and prodded them. The corporal shouted various expletives at us, casting doubt upon our intellectual abilities and suggesting we wanted to shake hands and become friends with the enemy. Then he told us to imagine that the German soldier standing there had just raped our mother and sister and then bayoneted our infant brother in his cot.
"Run at him; scream at the bastard for what he has just done and then skewer him on your bayonet. Stab him, twist it and then slit his guts open. Spew them all over the trench floor," he roared.

Much later, I would find out that whilst some of the reported atrocities of the invading army had been exaggerated, all too often there were examples of just this sort of barbaric treatment of civilians. However, it would be dishonest to suggest that Allied troops were completely innocent of unacceptable behaviour towards their enemy. War is a strangely enigmatic occupation; it brings out the most compassionate and courageous acts in some people, whilst others demonstrate their cowardly and most despicable nature.

All this was done to raise our adrenalin and hatred of our foe, and, no doubt, on the other side of the Channel, the Germans recruits were being conditioned in exactly the same way. It was standard military training. Before we could be engineers, we had to be soldiers. We were going to go into the front line because that is where the telephone cables were, and so it was necessary that we were trained as infantry for our own survival as well as that of those around us, should we be in the trench when an enemy attack came.

Living permanently in tents, even in the summer time, brought its own problems, the worst of which was the rain. With ten men tramping around in the confined space of the tent, the ground soon turned to mud. Whatever the weather, each day we lifted the bed boards, rolled up the sides of the tent and tied back the doorway. At night when it rained, we hung our boots up to keep them dry. During the late summer and autumn, fifty-two wooden huts were built in the grounds, some for accommodation, some for classrooms, and one as a medical centre. It was with much relief that we moved out of the tents and into the huts before the nights started to get too cold and really wet weather arrived. For the first time in five months, we had a bed to sleep in and, by comparison with the hard boards we had got used to, the three straw-filled squares called biscuits seemed like a luxury mattress.

After all the physical and weapons training, it was time for the technical part to start. Our job would be to establish and keep repaired the telephone lines between the various headquarters and the front-line command posts. The lines that were well behind the

Front were suspended from poles, but closer to the trench system, they were laid under the ground. In the trenches, the cables were strung along the edge of the trench, so as not to interfere with the troops holding the position.

In France.
As mounted troops we were issued with ammunition bandoliers.
I'm wearing my puttees as well as the bandolier in this picture.

Chapter Nine

"It was not part of their blood,
It came to them very late
With long arrears to make good,
When the English began to hate."
The Beginnings 1914-18 – Rudyard Kipling

D

ue to the pre-war preparedness of the German military machine, their artillery was much better supplied with shells than were the British in the early stages of the conflict. The shortage of British shells had been of growing concern since late 1914, and by early the following year, it had become critical. The C-in-C, Field Marshal Sir John French, gave an interview to *The Times* on 27th March in which he made this shell shortage public and called for more production, attributing the high British casualties at the battle of Neuve Chapelle to this lack of artillery ammunition. This effectively placed the blame upon Kitchener, who was Secretary of State for War and with whom French increasingly disagreed. Their conflict of personality was not helped by the fact that both men held the rank of Field Marshal, although Kitchener's role was no longer as a Royal Engineer officer but as a Cabinet minister. Although Kitchener assured Asquith that the army had sufficient ammunition supply, the shortage had already been exposed in what became known as the 'shell scandal'.

There certainly was a shell shortage because the military planners had not anticipated the stagnation of the Western Front and the consequent high use of artillery shells in daily bombardments of enemy positions. Thus, munitions production lagged far behind demand. By way of example, more shells were fired by British guns in the thirty-five-minute preliminary bombardment of Neuve Chapelle on 10th March than in the whole of the three years of the Boer War. However, the shell scandal was more to do with politics than military procurement and was ultimately to exact a heavy penalty. Asquith would be replaced as Prime Minister of the coalition government on 6th December by David Lloyd George, the only solicitor ever to occupy 10 Downing Street, and French would be relieved of his command as C-in-C of the BEF in favour of his rival and former protégé, Douglas Haig. Kitchener would be moved sideways, no longer responsible for munitions production and would ultimately lose his life in a force 9 gale west of Orkney at around 7.30pm on 5th June the following year, when HMS *Hampshire* sank after striking a mine laid by the *U-45*.

The plentiful supply of artillery shells to the German guns meant that our telephone communications were much more severely disrupted than were theirs. It was, then, repeatedly impressed upon us that the job that we were to do was essential to the chain of command and to keeping the forward posts up to date with orders and information.

Finally, in May 1916, my training at Staple Hall was coming to an end. It had been considerably longer than normal infantry training because of all the technical information that we had to learn, not just about telephones, but also about how the army used them in the front line of combat. The highlight of our final two weeks at Staple Hall was being re-kitted. Although we kept the incidental items such as shirts, underwear, mess tins, holdall, and so on, our uniforms and combat kit were completely replaced with new issue. This included new SMLE rifles, oil and pull-through, a leather equipment belt, a bayonet and, since we were mounted troops, ammunition bandoliers rather than pouches worn on the belt.

We were also given the newly designed shrapnel helmet, later known as the steel helmet or, to the troops, their 'tin hat'. Until John Leopold Brodie's innovation came along, British infantry went into battle wearing their SD caps, which offered no head protection at all. Consequently, head injuries from impact, shrapnel and stones became one of the most common causes of death. The steel of the Type B Brodie helmet contained around 12% manganese and 1% carbon, which made it both very strong and non-magnetic. It went into production in October 1915. The shape of the Brodie shrapnel helmet has not only become one of the most iconic images of two world wars but, more importantly, it has saved tens of thousands of lives during both.

Since leaving Canada, I had kept in contact with my friend Iwan. In May 1915, just before I joined up, he had left Canada as part of the 2nd Canadian Division and sailed to England. He trained as a machine gunner at Shorncliffe army camp near to Folkestone on the Kent coast, where a few weeks earlier in April, a Canadian Training Division had been established. As well as a training area, the camp was also used as a staging post for troops destined for the Western Front, and so when their training was completed, the 2nd Division embarked directly from the camp to France between 15th and 18th September 1915. In February the following year, Iwan and his team became part of the newly formed 6th Canadian Machine Gun Company.

With as much information as he was able to get through the censor, Iwan had given me at least an indication of what life was like on the Western Front since he had been there. Consequently, by the time it was my turn, I did have something of an idea of the conditions there and the stagnation caused by trench warfare; but there was so much which he had not been able to warn me about.

We were given a week's embarkation leave, which I spent at home. Like everyone else training with me, I had been given a 72-hour pass for Christmas 1915 but otherwise I had not been home for twelve months. My father was interested in the telephone training that I had been having and my brother Herbert wanted to know as much about signalling as I could tell him. He was coming up to eighteen and would be conscripted if he did not volunteer soon. I knew that my parents were dreading the thought of both their sons being away fighting.

Lady Harnage gave Violet the Wednesday afternoon of my leave off so that we could step out. We went along the river bank for a little way and then sat on the grass watching the water drift and swirl on its way to the sea. Around us, bees hummed between flower heads and cattle gently grazed in the warm sunshine. We talked about what I was going to be doing and, for the first time, I realised that I was going to miss all this; the English countryside, the peace and quiet, the familiarity of all that I had grown up with; Violet. The thought that I might not survive sharpened my awareness of it all in a way that I had not experienced when I had emigrated to Canada. Sitting there on that sunny afternoon, Canada seemed so long ago. Suddenly, I needed to have something from all this with me and I asked Violet if she would write to me in France once I had an address.

I embarked for France on the night of Sunday 4th June 1916 as part of No.97 Draft, almost a year to the day since I joined up. After our leave, we assembled with all our equipment at Shorncliffe camp. From there we entrained to Folkestone. As a protection against the U-boats operating in the Channel, we sailed through the night, but even so, the dawn had long since broken by the time we arrived after a rough crossing.

Once ashore, we were directed onto a train to the Signal Depot at Abbeville, fortunately, as I later found out, avoiding spending any time at 'the Bull Ring', the notorious transit camp at Étaples. The great majority of the permanent training officers and NCOs at the camp had not seen service in the trenches but treated the men going through the camp extremely harshly, and often brutally. Some of these men were recovering from wounds received at the Front or were there for refresher training having seen action at the Front. Consequently, there was a great deal of resentment of the permanent staff by the transit troops. From August 1916 to October 1917, a series of mutinies occurred in the camp, resulting in the deaths of several people, at least two of which were by firing squad.

I stayed at Abbeville for the next three weeks, receiving more-specific training on the particular problems I would face at the Front. I was to join an Air Line Company and it would be our job to keep the telephone lines working between the forward headquarters and the front-line trenches. Normally I would have stayed at Abbeville a little longer, but on 28th June I was sent with two other lads to join the Signal Company at the First Army Headquarters at the village of Chocques, about two miles west of Béthune.

The morning was not cold but the heavy rain soaked everything and created a thick mist. We loaded all our kit into a transport vehicle that took us to the station, from where we caught the train to Chocques. At the station, a corporal with the Corps of Military Foot Police on duty checked our passes and directed us to the right train, where the serjeant in charge told us to put all our kit into a goods wagon and get in with it. We climbed in amongst the various pieces of equipment already loaded and made ourselves as comfortable as we could. We spent the next two hours making slow progress up to Saint-Pol-sur-Ternoise, where we were told to get out as that was as far as that part of the train was going. Whilst more wagons were shuffled around and coupled to the train, I saw something that I had not expected to see in France, a Salvation Army tea stand.

"Brew up!" he shouted to us, and we gladly handed over a ha'penny each for a mug of steaming hot tea and a bun. I was to find out that the 'Sally Ann' had tea stands in all sorts of places, even as far forward as under the gates of Ypres. Sitting drinking our tea, the sound of heavy artillery filled the air like the continuous rumble of thunder.

After half an hour it was time to go; a different goods wagon this time but no more comfortable. We were certainly not complaining, though, a door-to-door ride was much more than we could have hoped for.

The First Army was at this time commanded by General Sir Charles Monro, who had recently returned from the Dardanelles where he had successfully withdrawn our troops after the failed Gallipoli campaign. Monro had moved his HQ to the forward position at Chocques from Aire-sur-la-Lys two days earlier and now needed every available lineman to re-establish permanent communications to the forward positions. When we arrived at the HQ, there was an air of urgency and bustle about the place. All the talk had been of the 'big show' coming up. It was going to be the breakthrough that everyone had wanted in order to end the stalemate of the trenches. We had arrived in the hours before what was to become a passage in British military history to stand beside the Charge of the Light Brigade for immense courage and appalling losses, the Battle of the Somme.

The purpose of the plan, conceived by the French C-in-C, General Joseph Joffre, was three-fold: to draw German troops away from the Eastern Front, to relieve pressure on Verdun, and lastly, in what could only be considered as a triumph of hope over reason, to inflict crushing and devastating damage upon the enemy. The Somme offered no strategic value to Haig, and when told of Joffre's plan, he preferred an area in Flanders. In deference to British presence on French soil, Haig's policy was to give way to Joffre on such matters, though he soon became seduced by Joffre's plan, and in so doing, lost sight of the fact that the Somme had been chosen without identifying any strategic advantage.

Although the planning had started in secret, it soon reached the stage where everyone knew that a major offensive was about to begin, including the enemy; only the date and time were kept secret, and even that became self-evident once the bombardment started. Over the preceding months, a massive build-up had been under way. Men, guns, artillery, munitions and supplies of every kind had been pouring into France, and by the end of June, there was an urgency and expectation about everything, even to someone like me who had only just arrived. Haig, conscious that his Fourth Army, which would lead the attack, consisted of volunteers and conscripts who were untried in battle, had wanted to defer the attack until 15th August, but Joffre would hear none of it and became highly animated, maintaining that the German attack upon Verdun would have annihilated his army by then. The date was set for 29th June.

However, as the evening of the 28th approached, word got around that the attack had been postponed because of the heavy rain which continued to fall, not only soaking everything and making the ground too slippery for the attackers but also obscuring vital battlefield sightlines.

At the time, we didn't know how long the postponement would last; in the event, it was forty-eight hours, until 1st July. It had rained for the last six days and everywhere was like a quagmire. Conditions in the trenches must have been deplorable, with thousands of troops packed in expecting to attack the next morning. There was a little relief in that forty-eight hours but it would have brought little comfort.

The plan for the Somme was that the French would lead the assault from their sector, but the German attack on Verdun in February had drawn away much of the French forces, leaving the British to take on the weight of the battle. The heavy bombardment of the German positions started on the dull wet morning of 24th June and lasted without interruption until just before the attack began.

The rain eased late on the 29th and then a strong wind without any rain on the 30th helped to dry the ground surface. At 7.30am on 1st July, the whistles blew in the trenches of the British Third and Fourth Armies and French Sixth, sending more than 100,000 men over the top on a field of attack that was nearly fourteen miles wide. On the right wing of the Fourth Army, together with the French, there was much success on the first day, with their objectives against General Fritz von Bülow's Second Army largely secured. Much of the progress here had come from the artillery's successful targeting of the barbed-wire defences along the front line of trenches, allowing a passage through for the advancing infantry.

Whilst the German defences south of the Albert to Bapaume road had largely collapsed, those to the north of the road held commandingly higher ground and caused the British catastrophic casualties. Here the artillery, trying to cut the wire over two lines of trenches, was much less successful. Consequently, in places, the wire remained intact or at best with only small narrow gaps punctured through it. Once into the congestion of these confined gaps, those infantry that had managed to survive the shellfire whilst crossing No Man's Land were scythed down by the machine gunners like the summer hay.

German artillery which had survived the British bombardment now rained down shells upon the British trenches, where men were tightly packed preparing to follow the first wave over the top. Shells bursting in these trenches caused an inordinately high number of the deaths and serious injuries of the day. On that first day of the battle, the British Army suffered 57,470 casualties, of which 19,240 died. It would prove to be the worst day in the entire history of the British armed services.

Many of the men who died that day were from the Pals Battalions of Kitchener's New Army. The Accrington Pals in particular were decimated at Serre. That day largely ended the concept of the Pals Battalions because of the devastating effect that so many communities had suffered, where almost every family had at least one person killed or wounded and, in some cases, brothers, or fathers and sons from the same family were lost.

There is little doubt that a great many mistakes were made by senior commanders both in the planning and in the execution of the action. There was an inflexibility which Haig had built into the plan, leaving no room for local field commanders to use their initiative and respond to the situation that confronted them. Then there was the order for the infantry to walk rather than run across No Man's Land, so exposing them for much longer to the shells and lethal interlocked machine-gun fire of the defenders. Despite conflicting and increasingly pessimistic reports from raiding parties and German deserters, there was an over-confidence in the success of the week-long barrage having destroyed the considerable barbed-wire and machine-gun defences which protected the German positions.

The bombardment was the most momentous yet undertaken by the British in the war. Some 1,537 guns fired over 1,500,000 shells at an average of 8,929 shells per minute and it could be heard as far away as Hampstead Heath. There were, though, a number of factors known to British commanders which compromised the success of the strategy. First, it was too thinly spread over too extended an area, which, at Haig's insistence and against the advice of General Rawlinson the GOC Fourth Army, included the second line of German defence trenches. Although in the planning, account had been taken of the successful effect of shelling on the wire and defences at Neuve Chapelle the year before, the extra 5,000 yards of front and the increased depth to the German second line meant that the shell fall per yard of trench was actually considerably lower than at Neuve Chapelle. Thus did Haig misapply the value of the Neuve Chapelle experience.

To exacerbate the reduced impact of the bombardment, the proportion of artillery shells of all calibres which were fired during the week and failed to explode was unacceptably high; a legacy to the French countryside which even today is known as the 'iron harvest' and remains a constant danger as these unstable missiles gradually work their way back to the surface to be ploughed up. In Britain, there was immense political pressure to ensure that munitions production was constantly at its maximum output in order to avoid a repeat of the shell scandal the previous year. However, by the law of diminishing returns, as production output increased, there was a concomitant decrease in quality.

Next, the German defenders had dug deep into the chalk, creating underground chambers and galleries which at forty feet were far beneath the penetration capacity of the artillery shells sent over. These chambers were reinforced and provided sleeping accommodation, laundries, kitchens, first-aid facilities and, importantly, substantial quantities of ammunition. Some even had electric lighting, a rare commodity even in peacetime. Gun emplacements were sited in Ferro-concrete blockhouses with transverse communication trenches and defensive bunkers running through the whole network. The defenders sat out the bombardment and waited in the warm and dry until it stopped. That is not to say it was an enjoyable experience. The constant noise of the explosions above them, the fear of the attack to come, the lack of sleep and proper food took a heavy toll upon the nerves of the German soldiers. Nevertheless, their lot was somewhat more comfortable than the British and French who sat and waited in their trenches exposed to the rain, cold and basic rations for the days beforehand.

The four and a half months of the Somme battle would exact 1,043,896 casualties on the soil of France, of which more than 100,000 would die, and it would become one of the most horrific battles that mankind had ever inflicted upon itself. Whilst it is certainly easy with the benefit of hindsight to identify the many errors in the execution of this plan, a greater flexibility of minds by British senior commanders, and Haig in particular as C-in-C, could have not only saved perhaps thousands of lives but also led to a more successful outcome. In the light of the reports from the raiding parties and German deserters which were being made available to Haig during the days of shelling and which contradicted his expectations, the rigidity of the plan should at least have been reviewed. A more forensic analysis of the plan, which required men to attack uphill faced by defences built progressively higher, allowing the defenders an unrestricted view of the advancing forces, would have identified the magnitude of the task and inevitable consequences of its execution.

The men were weighed down with equipment, each carrying a sixty-six-pound load; some had additional items such as field telephones, boxes of carrier pigeons, picks, shovels and wire cutters. Whilst this was all essential kit, in the pitted, wet landscape of the battle it was, literally, just another burden to be borne preventing sleight of foot.

Haig was certainly willing to embrace new ideas, but whether he exploited the potential they offered to the fullest advantage is at best questionable. However, he cannot be left to stand alone in this criticism as the highest levels of command in all the major powers on both sides remained instilled with the cavalry ideal and a type of warfare which by 1915 they were only slowly and reluctantly coming to realise belonged to a bygone age. Of all the powers, the French were the guiltiest of this, and early in the war had suffered devastating consequences. The body of a man, no less than the body of a horse, was no match for a machine gun, but in July 1916 the lesson had still not been learned back at Joffre's HQ.

Nevertheless, the popular image of the Great War, and the Somme in particular, summed up in the phrase 'lions led by donkeys', which was attributed to the German General Maximillian Hoffman, is wholly misconceived. These were not Hoffman's words but, upon his own admission, invented by author Alan Clark seventy years after the war. Undoubtedly, there were many poor decisions made which led to unnecessary loss of life, but the British did not have a monopoly upon such failings amongst senior commanders. Whilst German officers tended to be more careful with the lives of their soldiers, by dint of their ages alone, most battlefield commanders on all sides had gained their experience fighting a very different kind of warfare and had not yet contrived a coherent and cohesive plan to deal with the stalemate which confronted them on the Western Front and the weapons which were available to their enemies.

Nor is it true to say that the generals sat and took tea whilst their troops died. Of the 1,252 generals who served in the BEF from 1914 to 1918, seventy-eight lost their lives on active service and a further sixty-eight were either wounded or taken prisoner. A casual look around the tragically numerous cemeteries from the war will reveal the considerable number of officer casualties, including very senior ranks. As a proportion of their numbers, officer casualties were significantly higher than other ranks, which is why so many of us declined the offer of a commission.

The tide of blood that washed over the fields of the Somme was, however, not in vain. In the short term, there was some small territorial gain, ultimately amounting to about thirty miles wide and seven miles at its deepest, though this was certainly not enough to justify the lives lost for it. In the wider context of the war, there were many lessons taken from the battlefield which influenced, moulded and directed future plans, and a great deal has been written about the Somme, probably more so than about any other battle in British history.

War is wholly indiscriminate in choosing who survives and who does not; perhaps fate, for better or for worse, is a little more selective. Amongst the attackers who survived the machine guns, the artillery and the mud of the Somme were the poets Robert Graves, Siegfried Sassoon, Edmund Blunden and John Masefield.

Others included two officers with distinguished futures awaiting them, Bernard Montgomery and Archibald Wavell. Another survivor was Henry Tandy, who was severely wounded in the thigh in the battle but who by the end of the war would be awarded the Victoria Cross, the Distinguished Conduct Medal, the Military Medal and be Mentioned in Dispatches no fewer than five times, becoming the most highly decorated private soldier of the British Army during the war.

However, with an apparent perversity, providence also spared and secured a pivotal role in history for one particular soldier of the Somme. Decorated with the Iron Cross Second Class in 1914, wounded in the battle and then decorated for a second time with the prestigious Iron Cross First Class 1918 was the future German Führer und Reichskanzier, Adolf Hitler.

The open slopes of the Somme up which our troops had to advance into machine gun and shell fire.

Mametz Wood, The Somme
The fine and impressive memorial to the 38th (Welsh) Division
which overlooks Mametz Wood at the point where they launched
their attack. Taking the wood cost more than 4,000 casualties.

The immense Lochnagar crater formed at 7.28am 1st July 1916

The Iron Harvest of the Somme

This shell was found at Martinpuich during the research for this book. It is about 14 inches high. Even after 100 years, unspent ammunition, shells, rifles, grenades and much more still work their way back to the surface.

The Thiepval Memorial on the Somme

The memorial contains the names of more than 72,000 officers and men of the United Kingdom and South African forces who were killed in the Somme region up to 20 March 1918 and have no known grave. Over 90% of these men were killed between 1ˢᵗ July and 18ᵗʰ November 1916.
The capture of the village of Thiepval had been an objective for the first day of the battle; it was finally taken on 28ᵗʰ September, such was the tenacity of the defending troops and the ferociousness of the fighting.

Chapter Ten

" 'Forward, the Light Brigade!'
Was there a man dismay'd?
Not though the soldier knew
Someone had blunder'd:
Their's not to make reply,
Their's not to reason why,
Their's but to do and die:
Into the Valley of Death
Rode the six hundred."

The Charge of the Light Brigade – Alfred Lord Tennyson

At the beginning of June 1916, the First Army was holding about thirty miles of the front-line trenches from Armentières to Vimy. North of us, the Second Army held the trenches from Armentières to just past Ypres, including the Ypres salient, with the Belgian Army beyond it to the North Sea. To our south, the Third and Fourth Armies occupied the trenches to just beyond Albert, after which the French held the line to the Swiss border.

The First Army HQ was set up in an old chateau near to the railway line on the other side of Chocques village, which those of us who didn't yet speak French pronounced 'Chockee'. The HQ would remain here until 16th August, when it moved five miles further back to Lillers. When we arrived from Abbeville, we reported to the duty RE serjeant, who detailed another sapper to show us where our billets were. I'm not quite sure what I was expecting, but it wasn't what we got. We were billeted in the old byre of a farm on the edge of the village but did have the luxury of relatively clean straw to sleep on. It was impressed upon us straight away that it was most important not to make any smoke when we had a fire to dry our clothes out because German spotters would bring down the artillery on us or on the Royal Flying Corps aerodrome not half a mile away at Gonnehem.

Chocques had been a typically quiet French village before the war but was now a frenetic hub for British troops. In addition to the aerodrome and First Army HQ, No.1 Casualty Clearing Station [CCS] had transferred to the village from Béthune. Needing to keep proximity to the railway network for the evacuation to base hospitals or England of the most seriously injured men, on 28th January 1915, after having been repeatedly on the receiving end of the enemy's 15 inch shells in its forward position at Béthune, the CCS had retreated the two miles to Chocques and had become well established barely eight miles behind the trenches of the La Bassée front line. The line had been set only after several weeks of intense fighting around La Bassée and nearby Neuve Chapelle in the first battle for that town during 1914 and 1915.

Whilst Chocques was out of range of most of the enemy's smaller artillery pieces, it was well within range of their bigger howitzers. From time to time, an explosion would erupt without warning, throwing great fountains of earth and bricks into the air. We had experienced the sound of artillery in training but this was very different. It was a frightening experience at first but one which I quickly had to get used to. Shellfire this far back was very intermittent, although it became more regular the closer to Béthune we worked. Attacks from aircraft, both bombs and strafing raids, were another hazard visited upon us on a regular basis. Sometimes these attacks were simply random bombing sorties as part of the general attrition which each side engaged in, but at other times there was no doubt that the main target of these attacks was the Casualty Clearing Station in the old boys' school buildings near the railway and the abandoned, rather fine Chateau L'Abbaye on the northern edge of the village, which the RAMC Colonel had taken over and left Major Storrs to take charge of.

The 29th June dawned with drizzle driven by an increasingly strong wind. Breakfast was served from the cookhouse, which was in the old barn at the farm. Afterwards, I was temporarily attached to one of the HQ permanent teams. We loaded up the motor lorry with cable drums and set out towards Béthune to carry on the work already started. We broke off for something to eat around 12.00. Whilst away from HQ, we were self-sufficient, and on that first day I was treated to the joyous dish that I would come to know and hate so much, Maconochie's stew. Whenever possible, British troops had meat and fresh vegetables throughout the war and by 1918 a staggering 67 million pounds of meat was shipped across the Channel to the Western Front every month.

In the forward trenches and at other times when access to a field kitchen was not possible, we all carried tins of M & V, that is meat and vegetables in the form of Maconochie's stew. According to the tin, it could be eaten hot or cold. To heat the stew, it was necessary to boil the unopened can in water for thirty minutes, a process which was largely impractical for all sorts of reasons, not least the absence of sufficient water or heat, or both. Consequently, more often than not, it became necessary to eat it cold. The stew was supposed to contain prime beef, potatoes, carrots, onions and haricot beans. However, the ingredients varied and some versions were more inclined towards turnip, beans and onions suspended in a greasy gravy, upon which, when cold, great globs of white fat floated menacingly.

To make matters worse, the whole concoction tended to produce an unavoidable and unsociable side effect in all who ate it. In the confines of a trench, it wasn't long before it quickly became audibly apparent how many had been eating the stuff. Maconochie's has been described when warm as 'an inferior grade of garbage' and when cold as 'a man-killer'.

Archibald and James Maconochie from Lowestoft had moved to Aberdeen and established a fish canning business. When the Second Boer War started on 11th October 1899, the Maconochie Company won a contract with the British government to supply the troops in South Africa with M & V rations. The contract apparently had no termination date and so, despite that war ending on 31st May 1902, the ration supply to the regular army rolled on. Thus, with the coming of the Great War, the arrangement was still in place and Maconochie's simply stepped up production. There were times, though, when I did wonder if they were still using ingredients from the Boer War. It was never enjoyable, particularly for a country lad. Poor we may have been, but we had always eaten well and even more so when I was in Canada.

On this first day of tasting, though, I had time, water and fire to heat the tin and so was treated to the luxury of a warm Maconochie's inferior grade of garbage. It was not good, and as the war progressed, it never got any better. Nevertheless, the four lads in the team I was with, who knew all about the M & V rations in the tin, had a good laugh at my expense.

Once having re-established the HQ connections, the main role of the air line sections was to maintain the existing cables and to run in semi-permanent routes of four to sixteen, and sometimes more, lines. The maintenance of the wires and the repair of the breaks in them was a continuous battle. With so many men, horses, carts and motor vehicles in increasing numbers moving around the area, cable breaks were a regular occurrence as infantry paid little heed to the need for care around them. The backdrop to all our work was the constant thundering of the guns on the Somme as the barrage continued unabated for the extra days.

On the evening of 30th June, Chocques was a sobering sight. The ambulances were arriving in ever growing numbers. No.33 CCS, of necessity now based in Béthune despite being within range of the larger German guns, was full to overflowing and still the wounded, dead and dying were being brought here to No.1 CCS. That morning, one of the many Somme diversionary raids had taken place just across the canal in our sector at the little village of Richebourg L'Avoué in the Boar's Head salient, with disastrous results. Indeed, Lieutenant-Colonel Harman Grisewood, the CO of the 11th Battalion Royal Sussex Regiment chosen to lead the assault, was so appalled by Major-General Dawson's plan that he refused to order his men to go into battle on the strength of it, telling the brigade commander, *"I am not sacrificing my men as cannon fodder!"*

Grisewood was relieved of his command and posted back to England. The 11th was stood down to the reserve trench and replaced by the 13th Battalion with the 12th in support. In England a few days after the attack, Grisewood received the devastating news that not only had the plan failed as completely as he had foreseen but the three battalions of the Royal Sussex had been virtually annihilated. To add to the grief at the loss of so many of his own men, despite having sacrificed his career to try to save them, he also learned that his younger brother was amongst those killed. A platoon commander in D Company of the 11th, Lieutenant Francis Grisewood had been hit by machine-gun fire whilst leading his men.

The three Grisewood brothers from Bognor had joined up together in 1914. The middle brother, Captain GMJA Grisewood, had been the battalion adjutant but had died three months earlier. Lt. Col. Grisewood returned to France in 1917 as CO of the 17th Manchesters and commanded them until he became the victim of a gas attack which ended his active service.

This ill-conceived, ill-equipped and foolhardy raid, cautioned against by senior commanders, cost the lives of nearly four hundred men, with in excess of another seven hundred wounded, most of whom came from a small part of Sussex. Amongst the dead were seven sets of brothers, including three of the four Pannell boys from Worthing, William, Charles and Alfred; the fourth became a prisoner of war. Amongst the many acts of great courage that day, one in particular stood out above the rest and CSM Nelson Carter of the 4th Company 12th Battalion was awarded the Victoria Cross both for actions against enemy positions and for repeated sorties into No Man's Land to rescue wounded comrades.

It was impossible not to be sensitive to the terrifying experience which all these men had suffered in the action, which, for the great majority of them, had been their first and, for too many, their last. The machine guns of the defenders had exacted a dreadful toll. The CCS staff at the old boys' school and at the Chateau L'Abbaye could not deal with the influx of men, some with the most horrific injuries, at the rate at which they were coming in. Lying on stretchers in the evening sunlight, these men, some little more than boys, who only a few hours ago were fit, strong, courageous fighters, now presented a pitiful sight. In intense pain, some sobbed uncontrollably whilst others cursed their wounds. A few, with wide unblinking eyes staring at something no-one else could see, would shout and point. Others still, with no future, lay motionless and silent upon the canvas sheets, their lives slipping away in the warm oozing blood that stole from their macerated bodies.

The ambulances queued in the town to unload their human cargo before returning to the Field Dressing Stations for more, and all this on the eve of what was supposed to be the big breakthrough. It did not bode well for the following day and was a grim introduction to what awaited me.

Then, at about 7am the next morning of 1st July, we became aware that, twenty-five miles away, the guns had stopped; we knew then that the attack was about to begin. The trouble was, just as they had known the day before at Richebourg, the enemy too knew that it was about to begin. They were ready and waiting, and we had seen the consequences the night before.

Despite the catastrophe of the Royal Sussex, there was a general feeling of great optimism around HQ that morning when we left to lay the next section of cabling. Before we returned in the evening we already knew that things had gone very badly wrong. Signallers are always the first to know good and bad news, even before the generals know it. That early optimism which had pervaded our headquarters in the morning had increasingly turned to concern and then dismay as the scale of the casualties began to filter through. It was clear to us all that whatever the plan was, it had not worked, and I could only wonder at the abject terror experienced by so many of those young lads who had gone over the top for the first and last time in the pale morning sunshine.

During the course of the nine days that I was in Chocques, we ran dozens of telephone lines into Béthune. Outside the HQ, the telegraph poles using the trestle system generally had twelve arms, each carrying four lines. The further forward the lines carried, the more dispersed they became, until ultimately arriving at individual destinations, which might be the Division Signal office and then on to the forward command posts in the trenches. Timber was a valuable and scarce commodity and so telegraph poles were a luxury only seen well behind the lines. Once destroyed, they were rarely renewed and so our cables were, of necessity, strung between any suitable standing object that offered itself. The closer to the heavily shelled areas we got, the fewer options we had. Sometimes a tree, stripped bare of all but one of its branches, would offer up its gaunt remaining arm for the cables, as a wounded man would reach out to the stretcher bearers.

Other opportunities would be found within the remains of buildings or lamp standards, their lights long since extinguished and often twisted by shellfire into bizarre shapes, but for us now finding valuable new purpose as telegraph poles. Because of the variety of supports and unusual methods that we used to run the cables through, these lines had become known as 'comic lines', the term even finding its way into the official jargon and training manual of the RE Signals.

At the start of the war, wireless was in its infancy and lightweight portable sets were still some years away in the future. When the British Army crossed the Channel to confront the advancing Germans, it possessed only four wireless sets. One of these sets remained at the BEF General HQ and the other three were taken by the cavalry. With the halting of the mobile invasion advance and beginning of static trench warfare, a reliable communication system between the various interlocking levels of command was needed, and it was the job of the RE to provide a solid wire telephone connection, actually thousands of them, all the way from the GHQ to each part of the front lines.

Major cable junctions were heavily camouflaged against enemy aircraft observation and at some points were even buried. By the time the cables got to Béthune, they all had to be buried for as far forward as practical because the risk to disruption of air lines by artillery was too great. It didn't take me long to realise just how highly dangerous the work of running cables that close to the front line was, whether as air lines or as buried cables. The shellfire, whilst rarely continuous, came in irregular and random bursts. It was necessary to develop a sense of fatality about it as soon as possible whilst always remaining alert and ready to dive for cover. Sometimes it was carefully targeted, at others it appeared to be just random shelling into the rear areas behind our lines, as we did to theirs, to cause as much discomfort and disruption as possible to resting troops and supply lines. Artillery fire was the single greatest cause of fatalities during the war; many more than deaths from machine-gun fire.

However, what we feared the most were the snipers. In the trenches we were more prepared for them and kept our heads well down when mending the cables, but in the rest areas behind the lines the first anybody knew that a sniper was active was when someone was hit. Although the British used snipers as well, in the early part of the war, the German ones were generally better trained and equipped with more telescopic sights and specialist camouflage techniques, sometimes hiding below ground and using a periscope contraption attached to the rifle. That way we couldn't even see the person shooting at us. They were capable of remaining in one hiding place for days on end, slowly taking a toll and instilling great fear. Favourite places would be overlooking our water sources, which were inevitably almost always exposed.

The German sniper was largely independent, staying in the area for months on end, if we didn't get him. By doing so he could study the weaknesses in our defences – any dip in the sandbag wall or a shallow trench, the pathways we used above ground at night and the position of our loopholes. Trees were a favoured hiding place for them; although that wasn't a problem we had as there were no trees left standing around Cuinchy by 1916. The Brickstacks was their favourite hideout opposite us. In contrast, British snipers were attached to their own battalions and therefore moved with them every few days, unable to benefit from becoming familiar with their surroundings.

It wasn't until early 1916 that the British senior command began to recognise both the human cost of sniping and thus, conversely, its great value. On peacetime English country estates there had been a culture of reluctance to use the telescopic sight, considering it to be unsportsmanlike, as indeed was the idea of sniping per se. Our continental adversaries had no such qualms. They had embraced the advent of the sights and were adept in their use.

Part of what changed British minds was the attitude of the colonial forces, especially the Canadian Expeditionary Force. Used to hunting game in the forests and frozen wastes, some of these men were extraordinary shots. It was a First Nation Canadian soldier, Corporal Francis Pegahmagabow, 'Peggy', of the Wasauksing who became the Allies' most successful sniper and scout of the war, with 378 confirmed kills and an unknown number of probables. He served in France and Belgium throughout the war and saw action all along the Front, including at Ypres, the Somme and Passchendaele. Using the hunting skills he learned as a young man, he soon began to make his presence felt wherever he was. He was awarded the Military Medal with two bars, in the process becoming the most highly decorated First Nations man in the war.

On 7th July I was posted to my permanent unit, the 52nd Motorised Air Line Section based in the forward position at the coalmining village of Béthune. It was from here that I would work in the trenches. It was raining on and off that morning but I managed to get a lift for most of the way to Béthune. After that I walked until I found my unit on the eastern side of the town. The road into the settlement, which had been churned up by heavy shelling and the constant passage of vehicles in the heavy rains over the last fortnight, was very slippery. Holding my kitbag on my shoulder with one hand and carrying my rifle in the other, it became quite an effort to keep my balance whenever I had to get off the road a bit smartly as one after another motor lorry or horse-drawn cart trundled past.

There was a lot of activity and noise going on around me and it was not easy to hear the vehicles coming up from behind me on the narrow road. The sound of artillery fire from the not-too-distant front was a constant backdrop to the noise of the general activity along the road. It wasn't long before I had to step aside to let a field ambulance wagon drawn by two weary horses plod by. Passing barely two feet from me, the wagon's large red cross on its side was liberally splattered with mud, and from inside, even above all the clattering noise around, I could hear the agonised cries of the occupants as the wagon thumped and bumped its way along the road which was pitted with hastily filled in shell holes. For a few minutes I watched the ambulance slowly lurch away towards the railhead at Béthune. As I did so, I was struck by an unnerving premonition. My blood turned icy cold and a violent shiver passed through my body.

I found the unit conveniently based in what had once been a small workshop on the east side of the town, still complete with many of the tools of its previous occupier. I reported to the officer, a young lieutenant who welcomed me to the section, told me to get a mug of tea and something to eat then report back to him.

In 1916, the strength of the air line sections was increased. We no longer used horses this close to the front line, although many other units did, and so our farriers, shoeing smiths, drivers and spare horse drivers were all dispensed with, but the number of permanent linemen sappers was brought up from thirty-three to forty, together with an additional lineman corporal, making the section fifty-nine when at full strength. I was part of that 1916 increase which had been planned for during the previous year.

When I reported back to the officer, he allocated me to one of the two teams, each headed up by a serjeant. I was there to replace a sapper who had been killed a few days earlier, caught in artillery shelling. The system which the officer worked was to have one team in the section of the trenches whilst the other team covered the area to the rear and the town, and then change us over after about a fortnight. In practice, though, it was a much more fluid system, often entailing longer periods at the front when enemy shelling had been particularly heavy or the weather consistently wet, which it so often seemed to be.

171

The Béthune billet was in the cellars underneath what was left of the three houses next door to the workshop. The cold stone walls of the cellars were damp and the smell in the room where I was to sleep was a musty concoction of feet, sweat, methane, mud and the ubiquitous cordite. Any wine which had been left behind by the owners had long since been drunk.

The men that I was to share my foreseeable life with seemed a friendly bunch. Most of them had been here for some months and had inevitably become hardened to life as it was. Our bedding was the usual straw, which was always in short supply. The bed straw of the dead sapper I had been sent to replace had disappeared amongst the other bedding so the corporal told me that if I wanted something to lie on that night I needed to go and fetch some fresh from the Field Ambulance stables across the road, but whatever else I did, make damned sure that I didn't get caught.

By fresh straw, he meant from off the floor of the stables. I quickly crossed the road and went into the stable yard. A farrier was engrossed busily working on a horse at the far end. There was no-one else in sight. I slipped into the nearest stable, but it was completely bare, having been washed out, as was the next one. The farrier now had his back to me and so I was able to quietly cross the yard to the opposite block. Here there was plentiful new straw on the floor, but in the corner lay three quarters of a clean bale. I gathered it up and, after checking that the farrier was still busy with the horse, furtively dodged back out of the yard and returned to the cellar.

When I walked through the door with my great armful of fresh straw, everyone in the room was in fits of laughter. I had been set up. The Field Ambulance unit stable men guarded the straw for its horses very jealously and no-one had yet been able to relieve them of any, which is why the lads thought it a great laugh to send me there, certain that I would get caught and be sent packing with plenty of abuse to follow me. Whilst I was gone, one of them had been to the Quartermaster Serjeant and drawn my meagre straw ration for me. Realising that their joke had backfired and that I now had a double straw ration, they wanted to know how I had succeeded. I told them something of my time in Canada and shared the extra straw around, which did much to ingratiate me to them.

Two days later, after the evening meal, we headed for the trench system and our forward billet, which was another cellar under the remains of a house in Cuinchy. It had been overcast all day and had become very hot with no wind at all; the night brought little change. The hamlet of Cuinchy, together with the nearby larger village of Cambrin, had become absorbed into the British trench system and was about 300 yards behind our front line. Cuinchy was well beyond the limit of safe daytime movement, the risk of snipers, particularly from the Boar's Head salient and the Brickstacks, posed a real threat whenever anyone was moving around and thus the trenches had of necessity spread around the ruined houses rather like the roots of a plant around a large stone. However, with the hamlet sitting so close to the front line and well within German machine-gun and light artillery range, with typical soldiers' humour Cuinchy was of course known to one and all as Cushy.

Whenever possible, heavy and bulky equipment such as ammunition, barbed wire, wooden posts and so on was moved up to the front by the railway system. This was either on the existing tracks or new ones laid by the Royal Engineers Light Railway companies. Béthune, about seven miles behind the front lines, was our forward depot. From there on, it was carried by pack horses, carts or men. We were fortunate to have a 30cwt truck to carry our equipment most of the way. We loaded our packs, rifles, ammunition bandoliers, tools and rolls of cables into the back and set out to drive along the narrow road, which was now little more than a rutted track, towards Cambrin. From wherever we stopped, it was by foot for the rest of the way, which meant carrying everything we needed to Cuinchy through the trench system, although at night we were generally able to use surface tracks so long as no flares were being put up by either side. The water table was very close to the surface along this part of the Front and the ground was sodden, even at the beginning of July. The rain and the heavy use of this one track over many months had churned it into an almost impassable state, despite efforts to repair it.

About two miles short of Cambrin we abandoned the 30cwt to our driver and set out along the road loaded down with our equipment. It is surprising how quickly the eyes become accustomed to seeing in the dark, or more exactly in the pale darkness of the summer time. Despite this, we stumbled along under the burden of the heavy rolls of cable together with all our equipment, accompanied by the occasional 'bugger it' and 'bloody road' from a couple of the lads who had been doing this trip for many months now.

At Cambrin it was no longer safe to be on the road and we dropped into one of the trenches that would eventually lead us to our billet. Our arrival at the ruined house that acted as our base was greeted with much relief from the other team, who gladly handed over, quickly gathered up their belongings and kit, and left to retrace our steps back to the comparative safety and quiet of Béthune.

The Battalion HQ was a damaged house in Cambrin and the job for us in the forward unit was to ensure that the telephone lines between Béthune, BHQ and the front trenches were kept intact. Enemy artillery and bombing was the main cause of broken wires but we had other causes to contend with, which included the inadvertent actions of our own men and the constant gnawing of rats. In the trenches, the cables were stapled to the parados, the rear edge of the trench, and the constant passage of men, supplies and equipment and prolonged periods of rain all helped to make the staples unstable. Once that happened, the cables sagged and were prone to snagging and breakages as men ducked underneath them and they became entangled in equipment. We would go into the trenches in the daytime to see where the breaks were and if possible repair them without getting our heads blown off by a sniper. Once they had been repaired, we returned at night time when, under cover of darkness, we could re-staple them to the parados or lay new cables along the communication trenches.

The basic model for the trench system was of three lines of zigzag trenches, connected by a regular pattern of communication trenches, sometimes extending more than half a mile, also zigzagged and which ran roughly at right-angles to the other three lines. The front line was the main attack/defence position. This was the most exposed and dangerous. It was from here that patrols would be sent out most nights to listen to what the enemy were doing or to carry out bombing raids, which involved crawling close to the German front line and lobbing bombs, later known as Mills bombs, or hand grenades, into their trenches. They of course did the same to us. In the early part of the war, the bombers had to make their own hand grenades from the basic ingredients and these were inevitably far inferior to the German manufactured percussion stick grenade, known by all as 'the potato masher'. However, by 1916, the Mills bomb hand grenade was standard issue to British troops and was a very effective weapon.

Sometimes a sap, a short trench from where the name sapper originates, would be dug out towards the enemy lines. This would allow a better listening position of the enemy's activities and could also be used as a point from which to bomb the German front line.

The theory was for the front trench to be dug about seven feet deep and six feet wide. For two or three feet, and often more, on top of both the parapet and the parados, a network of tightly packed interlocking sandbags full of soil would be built to absorb bullets and shrapnel, give added protection and create a last obstacle to an attacking force. Dugouts were created along the communication trenches, although all too often these quickly became waterlogged and were rarely deep enough to withstand heavy artillery shelling. A fire step of about two feet high was cut into the front wall of the trench to allow sentries, officers and rifle fire defenders to stand on and see above or through the defences, but generally only at night, otherwise a sniper would be sure to have another victim. During daylight hours, a periscope contraption would be used and these too became regular targets for the German snipers. This front line would be strengthened, ideally about every eight yards, by a soil and sandbag island traverse around which the trench would wind. The zigzagging and winding were to prevent the enemy, should he get into the trench, from pouring enfilade fire down its length, killing all in sight. Several yards deep of barbed wire with little alleyways through to allow patrols and raiding parties to get in and out were placed several yards forward of the front trench and the whole lot was then protected by machine-gun positions. From 1917, tank traps were dug in front of the wire.

This was the broad theory, but local conditions and the greater the time of occupation varied this structure. The network could stretch back three or four miles from the front line to where it was deemed fairly safe from all but heavy artillery fire to walk about. The trouble for the British was that there were few places along our Front where a trench could be dug seven feet deep because three or four feet down we would hit the water table. The Germans, on the other hand, whilst retreating from the Battle of the Marne in 1914, had chosen where to stop, dig in and make a stand. Thus they had the pick of the land, which included most of what few hills there were in this part of northern France and Belgium.

Despite trying to drain the trenches and to install sumps, the ground was always sodden, even in good weather, and it took very little rain to turn it all into a morass of muddy sludge. To help with the waterlogging, we used duckboards, but generally, the living conditions in the British trenches were far worse than they were for the Germans and, more importantly, because theirs were generally on the higher ground, they were able to dig down much deeper than we were and so remain both dry and safe from artillery bombardment, which was exactly what had gone wrong with the attack on the Somme. Nevertheless, it wasn't always so for them, and one of few consolations that we had along this stretch was that because the enemy lines were so close, we knew that he was having to suffer the same hardships of wet and rats that we were.

Behind the front line was the support trench which held the next line of defenders, living in the same conditions as the front line. Behind that was the reserve trench which might hold a battalion HQ, officers' dugouts and cooking facilities. Officers serving in the front two trenches lived under the same conditions as the men, although usually with a dugout containing a table and rough bed. The table was a necessity for the officer because, in addition to writing up the company's war diary each day, he had, on an almost daily basis, to write to the widow or parents of one or more of his men who had just been killed. Behind all that was the maze of alleyways and passages dug to allow access and egress by large numbers of troops and the delivery of daily supplies. When an attack on the enemy was planned, all these trenches would be packed with men waiting to go over the top in waves.

We lived in these conditions for years. The only way out was death or a 'Blighty' wound, that is, an injury so serious that you were sent back to England to recover. Generally, though, this was only a temporary relief, for most of those who went back to England to receive treatment were quickly returned to the Front again as soon as they were fit. Death was the only sure way out of the misery of these terrible trenches.

Cuinchy was located next to the Canal d'Aire and the trenches in this sector were particularly wet and shallow, almost constantly waterlogged even when it didn't rain. There were many occasions when we waded through water halfway up our thighs as we moved around the system. For days on end, men were never dry. Some of the telephone wires were run underneath the duckboards as a safer alternative to stapling them to the parados, but then the wires risked being cut by the constant trampling of feet over the boards.

Keeping to the duckboards became ever more important in wet weather as holes three and four feet deep quickly developed at the sides. Apart from getting even wetter by falling into one of these sumps, they were dangerous and could suck a man underneath and drown him.

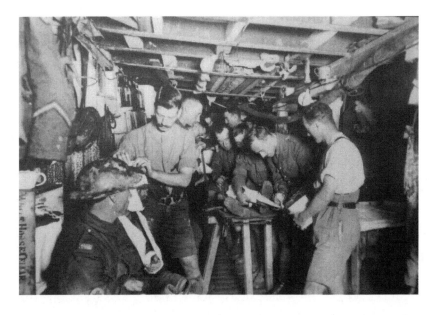

An Advanced Dressing Station like the one where I was operated on.
[IWM/CWGC]

No.3 Canadian CCS [IWM / CWGC]

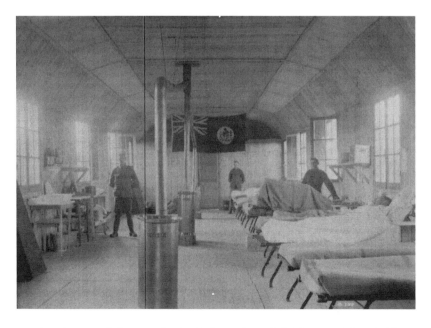

Inside one of the wards No.3 Canadian CCS [IWM / CWGC]

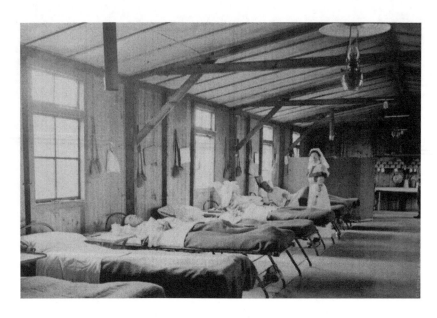

*The hospital at Remy Siding at Lijssenthoek, near Poperinge.
[IWM/CWGC]*

*Those lucky enough to 'catch a Blighty' on the start of their journey
back to Britain to recover. [IWM/CWGC]*

Chapter Eleven

" Tell me: an old louse, what does it fear?
It fears boiling water, boiling bubbling water."
Balzac and the Little Chinese Seamstress – Dai Sijie

My first spell in the trenches was with Stanley Harrington on the morning of Wednesday 12th July. There had been some drizzle early on but it soon cleared although it remained overcast. It wasn't so hot that day. We moved through the maze of passageways, all of which had either names or numbers to help everyone identify them both on the ground and on trench maps. On this first day, they all looked the same to me, a haphazard jumble of nondescript passageways which shared the one common feature of slimy mud. Stanley, who had been with the unit for many months, assured me that we were going down the Old Kings Road and that I would soon get used to recognising where I was, even in the dark. Up and down the system, the names reflected the regiments that had established them, and little street name boards were put up at the corners to help with navigation, especially at night when every trench looked the same. The Middlesex Regiment had spent a lot of time here fighting for this ground the year before and had named the different trenches.

We had come into the line to repair a fault on one of the telephone connections to a forward dugout and moved along with the greatest of care, keeping our heads well down. The Germans held the infamous Brickstacks opposite and had positioned snipers amongst them. The two front lines were so close together at this point that it was not unusual for conversations between the two sides to be shouted across the land in between, usually with the intention of finding out the enemy's strength at any given time. Both sides did it and both sides knew the purpose, so not much was ever given away, but it could lead to some amusing exchanges.

Some of the battalion holding that section were busy repairing the fire steps, others were cleaning their rifles, whilst a few were trying to cook some breakfast. An officer was watching the German lines through a trench periscope whilst the opposing artillery batteries provided intermittent shelling which occasionally led to an explosion close by. Unaccustomed to being shelled, I dived for cover every time, which at least gave the infantry chaps something to laugh about.

There was mud everywhere, thick glutinous squelching mud that covered everything. In no time at all, despite the duckboards, it was over my boots and up my legs. My hands and the bag of tools I was carrying had mud on them, my SD had mud on it, and before long, my face had mud on it. I had to work in this muck but the men around me had to live in it for four or five days at a time before they were relieved to the reserve trench for another few days of the same misery. Only then were they able to fall back to billets behind the lines and have some respite, a bath, some decent food and rest. This was usually followed by a period of further training and then a return to the front line, although not always in the same sector that they had just left.

The smell of the trench stuck in my throat and made me want to retch. The latrines were located in saps off the communication trenches, but the smell that drifted on the wind that day was new to me. The breeze that wafted over the muddy ground lifted and brought with it a strange mixture of sweetness and sickliness; it was not the smell of death, that is an altogether different smell, it was the heavy stench of rotting flesh.

In No Man's Land, bodies of British and German soldiers that couldn't be recovered lay where they had died, and now in the summer heat were decomposing as they floated in waterlogged shell craters or wallowed in the glutinous mud, gorged upon by the ubiquitous hordes of rats. The risk of being killed by sniper or machine-gun fire was just too great to try to recover these bodies, and they had to stay out there. Most would lie there forever, never to be recovered and are still lying there to this day. By the time we advanced upon this mutilated, pitted and churned area of ground between the two front lines in late August 1918, they had long since disappeared to become part of the land itself. Underground mines, shell and mortar explosions, the ravages of rats, flies and the weather all conspired to carry them into the bosom of France, there to remain without a clue to future generations of their presence in some corner of a foreign field.

Although we worked alongside the infantry in the trenches both night and day when we were forward, I soon realised how lucky we were to have that damp cellar in the ruins of the old house to sleep in. I was later to learn that some infantry units resented the RE because, as a general rule, our conditions were better than theirs. We did not have to live in the trenches night and day as they did and we did not go on route marches when pulled back. On the other hand, the infantry were rotated out of the front line and received regular rest periods much more often than did the RE.

We traced the fault to a break in one of the many wires running beneath the duckboards. I already knew what to expect when we lifted the board. Stanley lifted it up and I waited, ready. As the board came up, a huge rat ran out from underneath with something sticking out from the side of its mouth. I struck the rat fair and square over the head with my trenching tool and it stopped, literally dead in its tracks; poleaxed by my well-aimed blow. I had grown up able to dispatch a rat with a shovel. It wouldn't have felt a thing or known what hit it. Somebody said, "Good strike, chum." I looked closely at the prostrate creature and realised that what it had been gnawing upon was still stuck in its mouth; it was part of a man's hand. I picked up the rat and threw it over the parapet. With some caution and, on my part at least, no little trepidation, we dug down in the mud below where the broken cable lay, but we uncovered no more of the hapless man. The body the hand belonged to lay somewhere else.

Rats infested the trenches, No Man's Land and everything within five miles of the front. They were everywhere. They had no fear and scurried about here and there as if we didn't exist. They came out of the walls and ran around the cellar in our old house near the canal day at night and it was a constant battle to keep them out of our kit. They ate any rations not put into tins and chewed everything and anything, including our telephone wires. Here in the trenches they were all far bigger than any rat I had ever seen on a farm and, whilst not quite as big as cats, they were certainly the size of kittens, having feasted for nearly two years upon the seemingly endless supply of decaying human and animal flesh that was constantly available to them. The old saying of breeding like rats took on a whole new meaning during that war. The only consolation that we had from the almost constant shelling was that, because there were so many rats, each explosion would be bound to kill several of them at a time, no matter where that explosion was.

As if the rats, mud, shelling and cold weren't bad enough, every soldier in the trenches of no matter what rank suffered the misery of chatts (lice). By now, I was scratching some part of my body every few minutes. It hadn't taken many days for the chatts to get into my clothes from the straw bedding, and so that evening, back in the house cellar, I took off my jacket and trousers. My skin was covered with the angry red sores where I had been bitten and then scratched. In time I would get used to them living in my clothes, my arm pits and my groin and would no longer scratch the bites but for now, I turned my clothes inside out, and with a lighted candle, burned them out of the seams, gleefully watching them drop off in their hundreds. Behind them, they left their eggs in row upon row of tiny shining black pepper seeds, and the sound of them popping in the heat of the candle flame added to the pleasure of my activity. I was learning quickly that there was no joy of any kind to be found in trench life. Getting rid of the chatts, which multiplied at an astounding rate, from clothes was a regular activity for troops throughout the war and was almost always accompanied by some sort of light-hearted conversation. If this is the origin of the word 'chatting' or 'chatting amongst yourselves', then it goes back to at least the fifteenth century; certainly a time when lice were all too common in everyday living for the whole population and this method of control at least as old as that.

Later, the darkness of the short night enveloped and obscured the village. There had been some shelling earlier in the day further to our right near Cambrin, but now the artillery of both sides moved into our section. It did not last long. Two shells exploded harmlessly not far from our billet and then an eerie silence fell across the front. In the trenches, the working parties would be out repairing the wire, building up the sandbags in front of the parapet, and at least one patrol would be out in No Man's Land.

I started to itch again and the irresistible temptation to scratch returned. Through a six-foot hole above me I could see the sky far beyond what was left of the roof. Unable to sleep, I gazed upwards at the stars which flickered against the darkness of space. Thoughts of such nights at home and in Canada crowded my mind; how had it all come to this? Suddenly the darkened sky was lit up with the brilliant whiteness of a flare, followed by the metallic clatter of a machine gun and men shouting. Then all was quiet again. I had no idea whether it was our patrol that had been seen or theirs. Later, I came to recognise the difference in tempo between our machine guns and the enemy's. Ours fired slightly faster than theirs; but they had more of them. Nothing else seemed to be happening and I drifted off into a shallow, uneasy, troubled sleep.

It seemed that I had only just gone when Stan was shaking me. "Come on, Rowland, wake up. We've got a job on."

The officer had received a report that the earlier shelling had severed the cable that ran between the reserve trench and our artillery battery behind it. It was thought that the break was about two miles behind the line. It was still dark and we needed the cover it gave us to find the likely location of the break before it got light. The cable at that point was a comic air line and we were going to be very exposed repairing it once the daylight came.

It was raining again, although not heavily, but a strong wind was blowing in from the west. The two of us, loaded up with cable and tools, set out through the twists and turns of the trenches, heading for the area of the Field Dressing Station. All was quiet. Although issued with them, we didn't carry rifles when working on the wires. We already had more than enough to carry and they would simply have got in the way. We arrived at the Dressing Station in the ruins of what had once been a very nice house with a large garden at the rear, and took a rest for five minutes before pressing on.

"All right, Rowland, let's go."
Still crouching in the trench, Stan flicked his cigarette end into a pool of water and stood up. I watched the red tip cartwheel through the air, strike the surface, splutter and die with a gasping hiss.

Once more, I heaved the cable drum carrier onto my shoulder, picked up the bag of wiring tools and my trenching tool, and whispered, "Ready."

I followed Stanley as we turned this way and that, slipping and sliding along the dark, wet corridors of earth. I tried to remember the names as we moved through the sections or to look out for any special features, but it was no use, it really did all look the same. From time to time, Stan would call out quietly, "RE cable party."

186

The sentry would acknowledge us and we passed along. It wasn't all that many months previously that a German spy had been caught in this area cutting telephone lines disguised as a Royal Engineer Lineman. He was shot by firing squad. Since then, our units had to be careful not to fall victim to an over-enthusiastic sentry who decided to shoot first and ask questions later.

We weren't alone by any means. The trenches were very busy at night with men passing through, carrying water, rations, ammunition and a host of supplies to the front line. We reported to the officer's dugout and began the job of tracing the break to the rear, following the line of the cable. A serjeant was sent with us to show us the way and warn the sentries.

"REs coming through, lads," and to us, "Watch out now, sump on the left. Mind the wire. Stand in there, stretcher coming through," as the stretcher bearers struggled along the dark narrow confines with a heavy casualty. Finally, "Okay, you two, there's the sap that leads out to where your wires run."

We thanked him and made our way along the short sap. A few moments later, I heard the serjeant saying quietly as he made his way back, "REs working to the rear. No pot shots in the dark, please."

We worked our way along the line for well over two miles until finally finding the break. A shell had landed close to the supporting pole and had broken all the lines that it carried. We started to work our way through the tangle of cables as the dawn slowly broke in the east over the German lines at around 3.30am. The usual dawn chatter of machine guns on both sides heralded the start of the day. The favourite time for an attack was at dawn, but if there was no sign of any movement and no heavy bombardment by half an hour or so later, the troops in the trenches were stood down and they could start with the domestic chores of the day, which included making breakfast, rifle cleaning, fire step repairs, general trench tidying and repair and, if possible, some sleep, for there was little chance of more than a catnap during the night.

The crater formed by the exploding shell gave us some protection as we worked until, one by one, the two ends of the different wires were identified and we could start to re-establish the connections. In the mid morning, the officer managed to get to see us and was concerned at the scale of the task. He returned to our base and detailed two others from the team to come out to us, which helped the job along considerably. Not least they brought us something to eat as we had not had anything since the night before. By nightfall we had finished and started to make our way back towards the reserve trench. Since it was now dark, we decided to use one of the tracks to save some time through the trenches.

We had not gone far when a flare went up, catching us out in the open and exposed.
"Get down, Roly," shouted Stanley, whilst diving into the ditch at the side of the track.

I was half a second behind him as the machine guns sprayed the track where we had been walking just a few moments earlier. Bits of stone flew over our heads and rattled around us. The flare died, the firing stopped and we lay very still for the next ten minutes. Finally, satisfied that it was safe enough to move, we quietly and carefully picked our way along, at any moment ready to dive for cover again. It was with some relief that we reached an access to the trench system again and dropped down into the relative safety of its walls.

"REs coming in," one of us said as we approached a sentry.
"Okay, chum," answered a voice from the darkened silhouette in front of us.

We slopped along the muddy system and reported back to the officer's dugout once more, tested the lines and informed him that all was now working again. The duty Signals officer in the dugout thanked us and we left them to it. Half an hour later, tired out, cold, wet and hungry, we clattered down the cellar steps of our billet. In the dimly lit room, our officer was waiting for us.

"Well done, chaps. Here, get this down you," he said and handed us each a ration of rum.

I took a sip and grimaced. The others were all looking at me, smiling, so I followed their lead, lifted my mug to my mouth and swallowed the treacle-coloured liquor in one go. God, I thought I was going to choke. It burned all the way down to my empty stomach and I heaved, coughed and cursed. Gradually, though, I began to feel the heat slowly spread through my body as the alcohol settled in me.

"Well done, Hill," said the officer. "Now get something to eat while you can."

On the small wood fire in the corner, a pot of Maconochie's was bubbling away. That night, it almost tasted edible. I slept without trouble for the next four hours.

A tot of rum was handed out to every man in the trenches each morning. The official measure was a quarter of a gill per man per day, which worked out at a third of a pint per week of navy-strength rum; that is no less than 57° proof. It was stored in one-gallon stone jars, each one enough for sixty-four men and marked SRD. Although kept under careful guard, in March 1918, two men did manage to steal a jar, which they then sat and drank between them. In the morning they were dead. SRD stood for Service Rations Depot but was universally known by one or more variants such as Seldom Reaches Destination, Soon Runs Dry or Some Ruddy Day amongst others.

The rum ration was introduced to the men in the trenches around November 1914 when the stalemate became apparent, the dug-in positions took on some permanence and the winter cold and wet took hold. The ration was greatly appreciated by the soldiers and even the teetotallers used it to rub on their feet to help guard against trench foot. Inevitably, though, there were some dissenting voices and they were exclusively from those who had no comprehension of what life was like on the Front, including the Temperance Society safely back in England, and a handful of senior officers safely far behind the lines. The most notable of these was the teetotaller General Pinney, who not only banned the rum ration to his 33rd Division men for a while but also tried to stop them from smoking and refused to issue them with steel helmets in 1916. The rum and the cigarettes were important for morale, but his steel helmet stance was altogether more serious as this was putting the lives of his men at unnecessary risk. There is no doubt that there were many fine senior officers during the war who were deeply concerned for the welfare of their men but Pinney was not one of them and played no small part in feeding the myth of lions led by donkeys.

Although he did not name Pinney, there is little doubt that Captain Alexander Stewart was referring to him when he said, "*The finest thing that ever happened in the trenches was the rum ration, and never was it more needed than on The Somme. Yet some blasted, ignorant fool of a general – damned in this world and the next – wanted to stop it, and for a time, did. The man must be worse than the lowest type of criminal, have no knowledge of the conditions in which troops exist, and be entirely out of touch with the men who are unfortunate enough to have him as their commander. He should have been taken up to the line and frozen in the mud. I would have very willingly sat on his head, as he was a danger to the whole army. Curse him. Those who have not spent a night standing or sitting or lying in mud with an east wind blowing and the temperature below freezing may think that I am extravagant in my abuse of the man who denied the soldiers their rum rations. Those who have will know I am too temperate.*"

Captain Stewart was speaking on behalf of his troops not himself, as officers were allowed alcohol in the trenches and usually had a bottle of whisky to hand. In addition to the daily ration, rum was also issued to the men just before they went over the top in an attack and to those who were detailed to do a particularly unsavoury task such as recovering bodies, especially from makeshift graves or from where they had lain for many weeks and were heavily decomposed.

As RE linemen, we were issued with rum at the discretion of our officer. It was strong stuff and could affect some of the younger lads and those former teetotallers until they got used to it, which they did fairly rapidly. Consequently, for us it was usually given at the end of a particularly cold job. I quickly got used to the taste and there was many a time when I was heartily glad of that warming drink, which we often added to a mug of tea.

For the next few days, the weather remained warm but often overcast. In the distance, we could hear the artillery guns of both sides as the Somme offensive continued to grind its fateful course. On 20th July, Private Albert Hill serving with the Royal Welch Fusiliers, and to whom I was not, so far as I know, related, was awarded the Victoria Cross for his action at Delville Wood. He was destined to survive the war and emigrate to Rhode Island in 1923.

After a fourteen-day spell at the Front, the teams changed over and it was a great relief to get back to Béthune away from the constant noise of the shelling, the wet, the mud and the trenches. Even though it was the early hours when we arrived in the village, the officer had, as I was to find out was usual, arranged for us to have a good hot meal from the mobile cookhouse. Feeling much better, we made our way to our billet for a few hours of blissfully undisturbed sleep.

My uniform was covered with dried, caked mud, which, after breakfast I set about scraping off and tidying up. By nine o'clock, washed and shaved, we were all looking a lot smarter and paraded for inspection. The officer told us that we had the morning to ourselves and could go to the shower baths at the local colliery.

The colliery was very good at making their showers available to the troops when their own miners were not using them. It was a huge building about 100 feet by 40 feet with a glass roof, which was remarkably still intact. There were about a hundred shower cubicles in the wash house, all kept beautifully clean and tidy. We spent around an hour here getting properly cleaned up, dried our uniforms and tried to de-louse them again. The fight with the body lice was a constant battle which we would never win. Only when we were issued with fresh uniforms were we free from them for a few hours.

I was still learning about living in these conditions. My boots and feet had not dried out for the days that we had been at Cuinchy. My feet were sore and had swollen inside my boots, making them so tight that I had some difficulty getting them off. When I finally did, I could see that my feet were red and inflamed. Once back at the billet after my shower, I went to see the Medical Officer, who gave me some whale oil and told me to rub it into my feet night and morning and to put some clean dry socks on as often as possible. The oil certainly helped and, together with the harder ground between the village and Chocques where we would be working for the next fortnight or so, my feet soon improved.

This time at Béthune was also an opportunity to replace lost and broken equipment or to make proper repairs if possible. The blacksmith's wagon was one of several essential visits when we were back from the front line. At Cuinchy all we could do was to make running repairs, but here there were more facilities as well as the stores coming down from Chocques.

Over those next days, we worked repairing, rerouting and camouflaging the airlines to the rear towards Chocques and forwards towards the Front. We were able to work in daylight here and only emergency repairs were carried out at night. Meals were all prepared for us in the cookhouse, apart from midday if a job took us too far away. At last I had time to write home to my parents and give them some idea of generally what I was doing, although not where I was. Up to now, all I had been able to do was fill in one pre-printed postcard by simply crossing out all the options that did not apply, signing and dating it. This informed my parents that, at the time of posting, I was well and still alive. However, even now, I could not put too many details in because all letters had to go through the censor. It was felt that what might appear to be innocent domestic chit-chat would give away important information to the enemy were a lot of letters to fall into German hands.

However, the real reason why the army introduced censorship was quite simply that it did not want the families back in Britain to learn too much about the war, just how appalling conditions were for their sons, husbands, brothers and fathers, how disastrous some of the tactics had proved to be, the scale of losses and of the shortages and shortcomings across a range of supplies from shells to gas masks. The first stage of censorship was by our own officers. In many ways, this was not a bad thing at all because it was from reading these letters that the officers were able to get to know and understand the men in their command much better than they would otherwise have been able to, particularly those who were experiencing domestic troubles at home.

I was very lucky because our officer was a good sort and took an interest in his men and their lives. As he did with all new members of his unit, he gave me some helpful guidance about what I could and couldn't write, which saved him time and me the frustration of having much of my letters scored out. It was, though, easy for him to read my letters home; I was single with no steady girlfriend and no problems other than those shared by us all. Some of the other lads were married or engaged and often wrote deeply personal letters. Our officer, like many in that position, refused to read them. There was an 'honour' envelope system for the soldier to confirm that the letter contained no classified or prohibited information. The envelope would be left sealed and the letter not read by his commander. In this way, a man was able to keep his private affairs private if he so wished. It was only partially private, though, as the envelope would be opened and the letter read in England by a postal worker, almost always a woman, before being delivered to the final destination.

Not everyone could read and write and whilst all the RE lads could as a necessity of the job, there were many infantry soldiers who couldn't. There were many occasions in the trenches during the day and back in Béthune when I would sit down and write a letter home for someone. For the most part, these men did not have the vocabulary to properly express their emotions. They knew what they wanted to say but were intimidated by pen and paper. I quickly gained a reputation for being able to write a good letter, sometimes writing several in one day. I was seen by many as being well travelled, educated and, at twenty-four, older than a lot of their contemporaries. The letters broadly fell into three categories, sad, happy and indifferent, and as long as the work was done, the officers were very indulgent because it was all good morale for their men.

I always started a letter by saying that I had been asked to write it for so-and-so, who was well and was sitting beside me. On occasions, though, it was heartbreaking to write some of these letters; men whose wives or girlfriends were seeing another man or had even gone to live with him, others who had received news that one of their children or a parent had died, others still who had found out that a brother or father had been killed elsewhere in battle. I had to try to find the words which would convey something of their anger, grief or even just their simple resigned acceptance of the inevitable after long periods away from home.

Others, though, were a joy to write. News of the birth of a baby, providing the man had been home on leave at the right time, of course, a family wedding, a relation who was reported missing having turned up well, or the award of a gallantry medal to someone they knew. Being asked to write a love letter was a little embarrassing, especially when it was for a man who had recently been married, but I soon got used to that.

The hardest to write were those of the third group; a letter for the man old enough to be my father, who had been married for many years and, although he undoubtedly loved his wife, and she him, they had nothing really to say to each other. After we had said that he was well and, for the benefit of the censor, that the food was good, he didn't have much else to say. There were many men like this.

Writing the letters was only part of what I was asked to do by these men; when a letter came for them from home, if they couldn't find a friend to read it for them, they would ask me. There was less of this to do than writing because most people could read at least a little, though sometimes I would be sought out because the letter I had written was sensitive and they wanted me to read the reply, or else simply they did not want their pals to chip them over the contents, especially if it was an amorous letter.

The GPO in Britain, together with the Royal Engineers Postal Section, did a truly outstanding job of taking the post from France and Belgium back home, and delivering letters and parcels from home to the troops right up to the Front. Twelve and a half million letters left the home depot at Regent's Park for France and Belgium every week, taking only two days to reach the Front.

19,000 mailbags crossed the English Channel every day. By the end of the war, two billion letters and 114 million parcels had passed through Regent's Park.

With 375,000 letters to be censored every day, it is hardly surprising that many officers became both weary and cynical about censorship in all but the most blatant cases, especially as the war dragged on and they too felt that people in Britain needed to know a lot more of what it was really like. The system was certainly rather hit and miss, because over time, my own family gained a fairly good idea of what was happening to me, and later Herbert in the Royal Welch. However, like most men, at first I spared my family details of the horrific sights I saw, but as time went on, I did share it when I could.

It was during this spell in Béthune that I first visited a local estaminet. I had drunk plenty of wine before the war but it had all been made by my mother from such things as gooseberries, elderflowers, and parsnips. Vin blanc was new to me and I didn't like it. The estaminet owner had obviously watered it down. Whether he did it to maximise his profits, minimise drunkenness or both, I know not, but I could tell that it was very weak. I stuck to the bottled beer, which was also weak but at least it tasted better. For all that, we had a good evening singing popular songs and laughing at the impressions some of the more talented lads were able to do until it was time to return to our billet just before 10pm when the bugler sounded lights out.

Chapter Twelve

"How sleep the Brave, who sink to rest
By all their country's wishes blest!
When Spring, with dewy fingers cold,
Returns to deck their hallow'd mould,
She there shall bless a sweeter sod
Than Fancy's feet have ever trod."
  Ode Written in MDCCXLVI – W Collins

Away from the Western Front, the Allies experienced both success and failure. In 1914, the Royal Navy was still the largest and most powerful navy anywhere in the world and dominated the high seas. When Archduke Franz Ferdinand had been assassinated in June that year, by good fortune, the Royal Navy was undertaking its annual exercises out of its base at Scapa Flow in the Orkney Islands and had a substantial presence in the North Sea of some one hundred ships. At the time, Winston Churchill was First Lord of the Admiralty and instantly recognised the potential threat to peace which the Archduke's assassination posed. In a profoundly astute move, he ordered the Navy to remain on a full war footing.

This order maintained the Royal Navy's presence in the North Sea and had the effect of containing the German Imperial High Seas Fleet to its bases at Kiel and Wilhelmshaven, thus allowing the 80,000 men of the British Expeditionary Force, their guns and equipment a safe passage across the Channel in that critical first week of August.

I am sure that there are many examples of events which occurred in the Great War only to be replicated twenty-five years or so later during World War Two. There are, though, three in particular which I think stand out above the others; two involving the Royal Navy and the third, the Army. The first was brought about by good fortune and courage, the second by the enemy's good seamanship coupled with British neglect, and the third by examples of outstanding soldiering.

The first of these events began on the 2nd August 1914 when the German light cruiser SMS *Magdeburg* had opened the Kaiser's war with Russia when it shelled the Baltic port of Libau. A little over three weeks later, on 26th August, the *Magdeburg* ran aground off the coast of the Estonian island of Odensholm. There could have been no worse moment for this unfortunate mishap to befall the ship, for barely had she struck the seabed when two Russian cruisers appeared. After a brief engagement, the crew surrendered and the Russians took control of the stricken vessel. A search of their prize produced, amongst many other items, three naval code books of immense importance. The Russians helpfully passed one of these books to the Admiralty, which, unbeknown to Germany, was thereafter able to read the Imperial Navy's messages for the rest of the war, including those sent before and during the Battle of Jutland, although it is doubtful that the Admiralty made the best use of this fortuitous windfall during the battle.

Twenty-seven years later in 1941, the crew of the destroyer HMS *Bulldog* would recover an intact Enigma machine and all the code books in not too dissimilar circumstances from a German submarine, the U-110. Depth-charged and forced to the surface, the crew abandoned their vessel, believing it to be on the point of sinking. But the U-110 was reluctant to slip to its watery grave and steadfastly remained afloat. Seizing the moment, Lieutenant David Balme led a boarding party into the half-submerged, wallowing U-boat and relieved her of her secret. Not long afterwards, the U-110 gave up and sank, ensuring that the enemy remained wholly unaware of the Enigma's capture, which greatly helped the code breakers stationed at Bletchley Park, next door to where I had trained in 1915, to once more read almost all German secret messages.

The second incident involved the Royal Navy Atlantic Fleet anchorage in the sheltered and protected Home waters of Orkney Islands' Scapa Flow. It had first been suggested as a base for the Navy in 1812 but the Admiralty had done nothing about it until 1905. Even then, the defences to the anchorage were sorely neglected by the pre-war governments and boom nets had to be hastily installed to protect the entrances to the Flow at the beginning of the 1914 hostilities. On 23rd November 1914, the U-18 managed to creep into Scapa Flow, hoping to sink a battleship. Looking through his periscope and seeing only a handful of destroyers at anchor, U-18's commander, Kapitänleutnant Heinrich von Hennig, decided not to risk his craft for a destroyer and turned to retreat from the Flow. However, whilst doing so, the periscope was spotted by a lookout aboard the minesweeper HMS *Garry*. Assisted by the trawler *Dorothy Grey*, the *Garry* rammed the U-18 and forced her to the surface, where Hennig was obliged to surrender. After the incident, the defences of Scapa Flow were quickly strengthened.

Six weeks after the start of the next war with Germany, on the night of 13th/14th October 1939, the British negligently allowed the U-18's infiltration of Scapa Flow to be copied by Kapitänleutnant Günther Prien in the U-47, this time with much greater success for the attackers and devastating consequences for the Royal Navy. Exhibiting great skill and seamanship, the U-47's crew slipped undetected through the scant defences at Kirk Sound and into the Flow. They cruised around in the calm waters, lit by the Northern Lights for an hour and a half, carefully choosing their targets. HMS *Repulse* had fortunately sailed that afternoon with the Fleet, but Prien was nevertheless rewarded with the silhouette of another battleship filling his periscope vision, the *Royal Oak*. Two of his three salvos struck *Royal Oak*, which sank within minutes. Prien also torpedoed the Atlantic Fleet's flagship, HMS *Iron Duke*. However, the crew managed to get her under way and beached her at Lyness. The Admiralty, though, kept this quiet, considering the news to be too demoralising for the British public so early in the war and having occurred in Home waters. U-47's crew returned to a heroes' welcome in Berlin, where Prien was awarded the Knight's Cross for his action.

The third event occurred during the withdrawal from Gallipoli. The 1915 campaign had floundered and then collapsed. The commanding officer, General Hamilton, was made the scapegoat, relieved of his command and not offered another one. As so often, the fault lay elsewhere. Only Winston Churchill, with customary foresight, recognised at the outset of war the importance of the Dardanelles to communications between Britain and its Russian ally's Black Sea ports. The War Office ignored Churchill's pleadings until the Czar asked for help, by which time, the opportunity for an easy occupation had been missed.

In addition to combat casualties, heat, flies, freezing temperatures, floods, a lack of drinking water and disease, dysentery in particular, all took their toll upon the troops that landed on the peninsula from 25th April onwards. In November Lord Kitchener visited Gallipoli and only then grasped the debacle which confronted his troops. He needed no persuading to order withdrawal.

If the campaign had been an unmitigated disaster, the withdrawal was a supreme success unparalleled in its excellence. Whilst recognising the need for withdrawal, General Hamilton feared that to do so would cost half the lives of the remaining troops. His successor, General Charles Monro, accomplished the evacuation of 35,268 troops, 3,689 horses and mules, 127 guns, 328 vehicles and 1,600 tons of equipment between 19th December and 9th January without a single loss of life to enemy fire; a remarkable achievement by any standard.

Evacuation was at night, the nearest troops, first in sixes, then in tens and dozens at a time, making three miles an hour to the shore to be ferried, forty to a boat, to the waiting transport ships. To avoid the noise of boots, a sandbag path was laid. Officers were used as backmarkers for each section withdrawn, setting explosives with delayed fuses to set off mines in tunnels. The very last man to leave the beaches of Suvla Bay on 9th January was Lieutenant-General Frederick Stanley Maude, always known as Iwan Maude. The man in front of him off the beach was Captain Clement Atlee, destined to be Prime Minister thirty years later.

In June 1940, Monro's tactics were evident in the Dunkirk evacuation and, four years later, they almost certainly influenced the thinking of Major-General Roy Urquhart when he planned and successfully executed a similar evacuation of almost 2,000 exhausted and battered paratroopers across the Rhine after the failed but valiant struggle for the bridge at Arnhem in September 1944.

In November and December 1914, sections of the German High Seas Fleet attacked the east-coast towns of Yarmouth, Scarborough, Hartlepool and Whitby, and in April 1916 they attacked Yarmouth for a second time, along with Lowestoft. Although the Germans claimed that these were legitimate military targets, the casualties were almost exclusively civilians and the raids seriously damaged what was left of Germany's moral standing in the eyes of the world.

Then, on the 31st May and 1st June 1916, 99 ships of the German High Seas Fleet and 151 ships of the British Grand Fleet finally met in a titanic clash at Jutland. The Royal Navy suffered the greater losses, with 6,094 sailors killed, including Admiral Hood, and a further 674 wounded. Fourteen British ships, the three battlecruisers, *Invincible, Indefatigable* and *Queen Mary*, three armoured cruisers and eight destroyers were all sunk. The hit on the 'Q' turret of Admiral Hood's flagship *Invincible*, was followed by a huge flash which travelled down to the magazine. The immense explosion which followed blew the ship apart, a fate which also befell *Indefatigable* and *Queen Mary*. The engagement had exposed a serious design fault in the Royal Navy's battle cruiser fleet and which largely accounted for the disproportionate loss of British sailors. German losses were 2,551 killed, 507 wounded and one pre-dreadnought battleship, one battlecruiser, four light cruisers and five torpedo boats sunk. Without a decisive victory, both sides claimed success, although in practice the glass was half empty for all concerned.

The British, with the greatest navy in the world and almost twice the fire power of the German force, should have prevailed. Bad luck which led to the loss of air reconnaissance, poor communication, poor use of intelligence and poor judgment, especially by Admiral Beatty, cost Britain dearly. The Navy was heavily criticised in the press for having failed to vanquish the Kaiser's force, with the tactics and leadership of Admirals Jellicoe and Beatty coming under close scrutiny. Within a month came the devastation of the Pals brigades on the Somme; a decisive naval victory would have softened this news for the civilian population. Nothing seemed to be succeeding.

For the Germans, their commander, Vizeadmiral Scheer, was also denied success. The trap that he had so carefully constructed to draw out and destroy a significant part of the Grand Fleet had failed, and so he did not realise his aim of redressing the imbalance of sea power between the two navies. Thus Jutland finally persuaded the Germans that another grand sea battle on this scale with the Royal Navy would not deliver them control of the oceans. History would go on to show that Jutland proved to be the last time that the massed ships of two great navies would meet in a set-piece battle.

Whilst militarily the outcome was inconclusive, it did have the effect of containing the capital ships of the Kaiserliche Marine for the rest of the war. The Germans turned to their U-boats to wage an unconditional war at sea in an attempt to starve Britain into submission. This was a strategy which the high command had wanted to use earlier, but the Kaiser had resisted it for fear of bringing the Americans into the conflict, particularly after the deaths of so many neutral American citizens on board the *Lusitania* and the strength of President Woodrow Wilson's response. German admirals, though, were confident that their navy was more than a match for anything which the United States could send against them and, after Jutland, effectively bypassed their Kaiser. Unrestricted submarine warfare was ordered. However, the Kaiser's reservations were well-founded, for in late 1917 the loss of American shipping could no longer be ignored by the United States and it entered the European war, turning it into a truly global conflict.

Away from these grand events, I had enjoyed the relief of dropping back to Béthune from the Front, but all too soon, it was over and before I knew it, I was packing my kit to move back to the cellar at Cuinchy once more. I had been nervous the first time that I had moved up to the Front because, despite the stories of others, I didn't really know what it was going to be like. Now that I knew what it was like, my nervousness had some rational foundation. However, as before, I found that the anticipation was much worse than the actuality and once we were in Cuinchy again with a defined job to do, my nerves faded away. It would always be like this; it never changed throughout the war.

We moved down to Cuinchy during the night. That day had been hot and the air was still and heavy with the smell of cordite and decay. There was little activity in our sector that night, but the following day was the hottest of the year so far, with afternoon temperatures reaching 88°F. Our own artillery was now keeping up a steady stream of shells on the enemy positions. It seemed that HQ was anxious to keep the enemy on his toes here and not to release any troops to move south to the Somme where the battle still raged.

The hot weather brought the curse of yet another pestilence upon us, that of flies. The rotting bodies of men and animals, the latrines, the contaminated mud, the heat and the damp made for a fly Shangri-la. The constant noise of the battlefield largely drowned out their buzzing but from spring to late autumn they were always with us. They swarmed around our faces in the still air, they landed on our food, they landed on our equipment and they landed on us. Like the rats and the chatts, they never left us alone.

I celebrated my twenty-fourth birthday up to my knees in mud on a dull, wet, sticky 16th August with the temperature having eased down to a more bearable 73°F. Nearly a quarter of an inch of rain fell that day and quickly turned the earth to a slippery, slimy quagmire. Even in the heat of the summer time, the ground underfoot never properly dried out. The constant movement of men along the duckboards, often slipping against the planking sides, resulted in the staples holding the wires coming adrift, sometimes within hours of us having renewed them. As a result, we were ordered to start replacing the staples with posts from which the separate wires were strung, not unlike the top of a telegraph pole laid on its side, giving the appearance of a multi-strand wire fence.

The work took us several days to complete as the soft ruddy clay ground would not hold the staples. It was necessary to carry out this work in daylight and so each day we were in the trenches ready to start before dawn. Just before first light came the daily order, 'Stand to' in readiness for an attack from the far side of No Man's Land, less than 100 yards away. By full light, all was fairly quiet and 'Stand down' was called. There were six of us working in pairs along the front trench. After the stand down each day we moved out of the communication trench where we had been waiting and into the forward trench. Not long after we started work on the morning of the 19th, the enemy's field guns began firing. It was not too much to start with and mainly aimed at our artillery positions, which quickly retaliated. The noise levels mounted as the gunfire seemed to blend into one constant sound. The ground vibrated either from our own artillery or the explosions of the enemy.

It was now that I came to experience the constant noise of heavy guns; the relative lull that had been a feature of my last spell here had been replaced by the steady roar and swee, swee, swee of our shells passing overhead. Cuinchy remained within easy reach of enemy guns throughout most of the war. It was not until well into 1918 and the wholesale retreat of the German army that the remains of this hamlet experienced any relief. Each side's artilleries kept up an almost constant exchange, which inevitably included firing shells into the opposing trenches. The whiz-bangs were the worst because you only heard them as they were arriving. It wasn't long before the stretcher bearers were needed further along the trench where the shelling was heavier. Even the rats were frightened. They would scurry in manic blindness in all directions, trying in vain to escape the noise and change in air pressure.

Now and again a shell would explode much closer to the front or the rear of the trench, showering us all in wet clay. The pieces of rock that flew up from these explosions were as lethal as the shrapnel that came with them, and the clattering on my steel helmet became just another sound in the constant booming, roaring and crashing from all sides. The staccato chatter of machine guns struck up to add to the terrible racket. It wasn't just the relentless noise that wore us down but the reverberations in the air which battered us as well. We felt every explosion through the very fibres of our bodies. We had a job to do which was made more difficult by the increased activity in the trench which the shelling caused. NCOs were trying to shout orders, officers checking the defences all the time, men either doing a job or taking cover in the dugouts.

Above all this terrible incessant noise, it was impossible to hear what was being said by way of any conversation, but standing very close to me and looking through the loophole on fire step sentry duty was a man I had chatted to a few times over the last couple of days. Private Armstrong was from Bury and a little older than most of the Manchester lads there. The roaring of the guns seemed to be getting louder and then three shells burst in quick succession very close to the front of the trench, sending great spouts of earth, shrapnel and rock fragments hurtling into the air, only to come raining down upon us a few moments later. Armstrong turned towards me and shouted something. I yelled back at him that I couldn't hear and I saw his mouth move to form the words once more as he repeated what he had said. I still couldn't make it out as the sound was lost in the clamouring din around us. Suddenly, his head jerked backwards, and as he slumped to the floor, my face was splattered with a warm spray of his blood and brains. The sniper's bullet had ripped a hole in the side of his skull. I was stunned into inaction. There was no noise any more; I could hear nothing of the terrible racket which just a few seconds earlier had filled my world and drowned out this man's last words.

I stared at the motionless body lying by my feet, then turned away and was violently sick over a passing rat which scurried by at the wrong moment. I started to tremble uncontrollably; I couldn't help it as I realised how close to death I had come too. Still gripped in my shaking hand, the pliers I was using began to rattle against the telephone wire. In that moment, I knew the true meaning of fear.

An officer came along the trench, looked at me and said something, but still my mind would register no sound. I felt remote from the scene I was witnessing; it was like being at the cinema watching a silent film. The officer turned to a serjeant standing beside him and must have ordered the stretcher bearers to be called to take Armstrong away. The gaping wound still throbbed blood to the rhythm of his flickering heartbeats. Unconscious, he clung to life without hope. The stretcher bearers arrived. I felt detached, a mere passer-by looking in through a window as events unfolded inside. I saw them stem the dark scarlet flow with a field dressing whilst the serjeant checked that Armstrong's dog tag was around his neck and that his pay book was in his pocket.

The men lifted the stretcher and awkwardly carried it away. The sounds of my surroundings began to soak through my inertia. I realised that my eyes were very wide and that my mouth was open.
"Are you hurt?" the officer shouted at me.
I wasn't. All I could do was just shake my head.
"All right. Carry on, serjeant." He had to yell to make himself heard.
The serjeant detailed a replacement sentry and everything just picked up where it had been; the terrible noise of the guns returned to my consciousness, the comings and goings in the trench resumed. I looked around me; it was as if the incident had never happened, as if I had dreamed it. Everything seemed just as it had been a few moments before.
"Leave that wiring, lad, and get in the dugout out of the way while this shelling is on," the serjeant bawled.

Lad. He looked younger than I was. Still gripping the pliers, I dropped down into the nearby dugout and joined the half dozen men already in it. It was no quieter in there and the ground shook more than ever with each exploding shell.

"Here 'ave this, chum," one of them shouted as I sat on the floor with a soggy sandbag for a seat. He thrust a tin mug of hot sweet tea into my hand and I drank it gratefully, washing the taste of vomit from my mouth. There was a small charcoal stove in the centre of the floor on which the char pot sat. The men mouthed short comments to each other, occasionally glancing in my direction. After a few minutes I began to feel better. The tea had warmed me.

Then one of them leaned close towards me to be heard, "You or'right now, chum? You should have come in 'ere sooner."
Only in that moment did I realise what it was that Armstrong had been trying to tell me. His concern for me had cost him his life. I had an overwhelming urge to cry. I didn't; I choked back the emotion and took a gulp of tea.

The sniper was in the Brickstacks and had been watching the loophole, seen the movement and shot Armstrong through the narrow space. He certainly wasn't the first person that I had seen dead in the short time that I had been in France, but the fact that he had been standing there speaking to me when he was hit did affect me. One day, long after the war was over, for no particular reason I thought about the incident and I did suddenly and unaccountably, shed copious tears for him. Private 9168 A Armstrong, 17th Battalion Manchester Regiment is buried in Chocques Military Cemetery. Unmarried, he had joined the army before the war to help support his widowed mother Emily. From the Calrows area of Bury, he was twenty-nine.

The officer must have telephoned our artillery because a few minutes later the Brickstacks were pounded with shells for some ten minutes. After that, the shelling eased a little on both sides and I returned to my job on the wires, trying to forget what had just happened; but the drying burgundy of his blood and the fading pink of shattered brains on my khaki green uniform were real enough.

By the time I got back to our billet in the Cuinchy cellar, the news of what had happened had preceded me and the other lads took care not to chip me about it. When sleep eventually came that night it was filled with images of the man's face, his words that I still could not hear even in my dream and the rent across his skull. In my dream he was still alive, still trying to say something to me, and all the time I was looking inside his head at his brains. Although I didn't have that dream again in France, it, along with others, came back to haunt me many years later.

In August 1916, we were still only issued with one dog tag, which caused problems with the identification of bodies. Somewhat belatedly, the following month saw the introduction of Army Order 287, which provided for a second disc which would remain with the body of a dead soldier. In typical army convoluted style, the dark-red round vulcanised asbestos tag now became the No.2 disc, which would be removed from the body in the battlefield or hospital, and the second disc, also of vulcanised asbestos but green/brown in colour and an octagonal lozenge shape, was to be the No.1 disc and would remain with the body at all times. My own octagonal disc caught up with me in early 1917.

It was in August too that I received a letter from my mother saying that Herbert had travelled to Maindy Barracks in Cardiff and volunteered as a signaller in the Welch Regiment. Like the Royal Welch Fusiliers, the Regiment used the archaic spelling of Welch with a 'c' rather than an 's'.

The Welch Regiment was formed in 1881 by the amalgamation of the 41st (Welch) Regiment of Foot and the 69th (South Lincolnshire) Regiment of Foot, becoming the 1st and 2nd Battalions respectively. An infantry regiment of the Line, the Welch has too many battle honours to list but includes every major offensive of the Great War. The Regiment also has six Victoria Crosses, including two from the Crimean War in 1854, among the very first to be awarded following the inauguration of the award. Three further VCs were awarded during the Great War and the sixth during the 1939 to 1945 conflict. It is perhaps an unusual though happy coincidence that all six VC recipients survived both the action which gave rise to the award and also the respective conflicts, each living on into retirement.

The last Victoria Cross of the six was awarded to Lieutenant Tasker Watkins, the first army Welshman to receive one in the Second World War. He had joined the army as a private soldier in October 1939 and after a year was sent for officer training, following which he was commissioned into the Welch Regiment. His award came in August 1944 when, with a group of other officers and men, he advanced across a booby-trapped cornfield which was being raked by withering machine-gun fire. As the last officer standing, he led his surviving thirty men in a bayonet charge against fifty German infantry, before going alone to overpower the machine-gun crew, thus saving the lives of his own men.

Watkins made major by the end of the war, after which he read law and was called to the bar at Middle Temple in 1948. He took silk in 1965 and the following year was appointed as Counsel to the Tribunal at the public inquiry, chaired by Lord Edmund Davies, into the devastating Aberfan disaster of 21st October that year, in which 116 children and 28 adults died when 40,000 cubic metres of a National Coal Board slag heap slipped down the mountain and engulfed the village school and nearby houses.

Later made a Lord Justice of Appeal, Tasker Watkins was knighted in 1971. A keen sportsman since boyhood, he became president of the Welsh Rugby Union, having played in the threes for the Army, Cardiff RFC and Glamorgan Wanderers, who to this day wear a green box badge with the embroidered letters STW-VC [Sir Tasker Watkins, VC] on the right shoulder of their shirts.

Chapter Thirteen

"Our brains ache, in the merciless iced east winds that knive us...
Wearied we keep awake because the night is silent...
Low, drooping flares confuse our memory of the salient...
Worried by silence, sentries whisper, curious, nervous,
    But nothing happens."
Exposure – Lt. Wilfred Owen, MC

By the end of August, the war had firmly entered its third year, with no sign of the much-needed breakthrough. The month had been hot with a lot of rain, preventing the treacherous slime on the ground from drying out. Whenever there was an occasional lull in the shelling around our own sector, we would hear the guns on the Somme, where the savage fighting raged on a few miles to the south.

Having returned to Béthune for a spell, we were out tracing new cable routes to the forward positions over ground which had been repeatedly shelled for two years. Apart from intermittent shell bursts some little way off towards the front line, we were able to work largely unhindered by the enemy. The cloud base was dark, low and heavy. Then, the clouds parted and through the hole a brilliant diagonal shaft of deep golden sunlight struck the earth and offered the poor tortured souls beneath an illuminated stairway to heaven.

Applethwaite saw them first. Two bi-planes descended that stairway about a mile to the south and headed straight for us, losing height at a steady angle. The pair flew in, one slightly behind and to the right of the other, their wings gently oscillating as they closed the gap between us. At first, we weren't sure whether they were ours or theirs and couldn't yet hear the sound of the engines above the general booming of guns, clattering of carts, chugging of motor lorries and ambulances, whinnying of horses and the regular thumping of explosions that, even in so-called quiet periods, formed the constant background chorus of every day.

On they came, lower still now. Then everything seemed to happen at the same time. We heard the engines and knew that they were not British; the crack of small-arms fire began to follow them across the pitted ground and the flashes from their own nose-mounted twin machine guns twinkled like sparklers. As if on an unspoken order, the five of us dived in all directions, rolling and sliding through the mud and stones, seeking shelter of any kind; a wet shell-hole, a broken wall, anything that would give cover. The bullets thudded into the gooey earth, kicking up fragments of stone, marking their passage towards us. Seconds later, the roar of engines filled our ears as the two single-seat fighters swept over the ground just a few feet above our heads. We lay in the wet mud as their slipstream washed over us like a refreshing breeze on a hot day. Each of us mouthed an unheard curse upon the pilots, the second of which grinned broadly and gaily waved a cheery goodbye to us.

Already climbing steeply, they turned to the east and headed for home, cloaked by the thickening blanket of the cloud which lay across much of northern France that day. Content that this had simply been an opportunistic attack and that they were not intending to return, we each cautiously emerged from whatever minimal cover we had been able to gain in our dive for safety. I recovered my steel helmet, spat a lump of mud from my mouth and wiped my face. Irritated, a little wetter and a lot muddier but otherwise unhurt, we five made our way over to the 30cwt truck which was undamaged and, in true British style, boiled up a can of water and made some tea.

Applethwaite, who was considered, not least by himself, as something of an authority on flying machines, had applied for a transfer to the Royal Flying Corps and was awaiting a posting. He announced with some certainty that the aircraft had been two of the new Albatros D1s and added that he was sure they must have lost their way above the cloud base, dropped down through the sunlit shaft to find their position and unfortunately found us as well. Since no-one had a better idea, we accepted this as a reasonable explanation but reminded him that since he was the senior sapper present, it was he who would have to write out the report for the officer. After that and much to our amusement, he offered us no further detail upon the incident for the rest of the day. This was not the last time that I was strafed, but it was the closest and the event remains indelibly etched into my memory.

Mater artium necessitas. At no time does necessity become the mother of invention more urgently, acutely and successfully than when a country is at war. Throughout history, wartime technological developments have far outpaced commensurate peacetime advances within the same field. The Great War was no exception and was witness to many, but it was aviation that undoubtedly proved to be the most significant, complex and far-reaching of them all.

Influenced by the out-dated military culture of cavalry generals and navy admirals, Asquith's pre-war Liberal government had been slow to grasp the significance of Louis Blériot's flight across the English Channel on 25th July 1909. By 1911, however, the military began to recognise the strategic advantage that aeroplanes could offer in a reconnaissance role. Relatively cheap, flexible, faster than a horse and with a bird's eye view of a battlefield, this new-fangled rich boys' toy might actually have some real purpose. In November that year, the Committee of Imperial Defence appointed a sub-committee to look into the prospects. It reported favourably the following February; a remarkably short period of time for a government committee. The result was that 13th May 1912 saw the Air Battalion of the Royal Engineers become the Military Wing of the Royal Flying Corps. With differing priorities, the navy's wing separated from the RFC on 1ˢᵗ July 1914 to form the Royal Naval Air Service, though on 1ˢᵗ April 1918 the two services would once again be combined to form the Royal Air Force.

By the end of 1912, the RFC had twelve manned balloons and thirty-six aeroplanes. That year, First Lord of the Admiralty Winston Churchill was tasked with establishing twelve air stations around the country. The first of these was RFC Montrose on the east coast of Scotland. Five aeroplanes of No.2 Squadron under the command of Major CJ Burke landed at Dysart Farm on 26ᵗʰ February 1913, having taken thirteen days to fly there from Farnborough; thus was RFC Montrose established. The site remains today as the home of the Montrose Air Station Heritage Centre, and nearby are three of the original 1913 hangars, the oldest of their type anywhere in the world.

Despite this programme of pilot training, Britain lagged far behind France and Germany in aircraft development and support staff infrastructure at the start of the war. Blériot maintained enthusiasm in France, whilst Germany, preparing for war, was fortunate to find that Dutch aircraft designer Anton Fokker had moved to Berlin and established his production factory there. The German government took over Tony Fokker's factory at the start of the war and the Dutchman produced around 700 aeroplanes for the Imperial German Army Air Service, the Luftstreitkräfte, amongst which the most famous was the bright red Fokker Dr.1 tri-plane flown by Manfred von Richthofen.

Aerial combat was born in the skies over the Western Front, and far below we stood witness to the evolution of its tactics from the Immelmann turn to the spiralling feint and the corkscrew. This latter manoeuvre was simultaneously but independently discovered by French ace Georges Guynemer and RFC pilot Lieutenant Roderic Hill, considered by his peers to be the best

British pilot on the Front at the time. Throughout his long air force career, he would be one of the most outstanding officers of the Service. Although he achieved the rank of Air Chief Marshal, and, from 1943, as C-in-C Fighter Command was largely responsible for saving London from most of the V1 bombs fired against it, his many and considerable contributions are now very sadly all but forgotten.

At the start of the war, all sides saw the role of their air force as a reconnaissance and observation service. Most aircraft were therefore designed for a pilot and an observer, and whilst the officers flew with a pistol to deal with the eventuality of a forced landing behind enemy lines, their aircraft remained unarmed. In the first few weeks of the war, it was the custom amongst aviators of opposing sides to wave to one another as they passed by each other on their patrols. Nevertheless, we were at war and the object was to defeat the enemy. As well as being the first RFC pilot to land in France, the accolade of downing the first German aeroplane in the war also went to No.2 Squadron's Lieutenant HD Harvey-Kelly.

Flying high above enemy-held territory with two accompanying aircraft, Harvey-Kelly sighted a lone Taube several thousand feet below him. Signalling to his section, he dived upon the hapless German, who, convinced that he was to be rammed, pushed his joystick forward and headed for the ground. Now herded by the three RFC pilots, the German was finally forced into an unscheduled landing behind his own lines. Abandoning his Taube to Harvey-Kelly, who had landed behind him, he made a dash into some nearby woods and disappeared. Unable to find him, Harvey-Kelly returned to the Taube, set it alight then took off again in his BE2 returning to his base at St Omer.

Whilst opposing airman largely behaved chivalrously towards one another, they soon realised the importance of preventing the other side's crew from returning to their base to report upon their observations of troop positions and movements. By a gradual process of trial and error, weaponry designed for attack was taken into the air.

At first, observers were given hand grenades, and sometimes even bricks, to throw. The futility of this was quickly recognised and the observer was then armed with a rifle which, surprisingly, did produce an occasional success. In the meantime, efforts were being made to arm these flimsy aeroplanes with more lethal means of destruction. Machine guns were mounted on the air frame, but trying to shoot over the top of the propeller remained a problem, particularly for the pilots of single-seat fighters. It was hard enough to fire one-handed whilst keeping the aircraft steady with the other, but changing the ammunition canister required extraordinary dexterity.

In early 1915, the French ace Roland Garros mounted a machine gun on the front of his little Morane fighter. To prevent the propeller being blasted apart by the bullets, he protected the cockpit side of the blades with steel plates. This was highly effective but equally dangerous to Garros, and he enjoyed much success until a fuel-line blockage caused a forced landing behind enemy lines. His Morane was captured and sent to Berlin, where Tony Fokker solved the problem and gave the German pilots the immense advantage of synchronising the gun to fire through the spinning blades. So secret was the technology that pilots of these aeroplanes were not allowed to patrol beyond their own front lines for fear that a downed aircraft would fall into Allied hands. Six months later, in almost identical circumstances, the Allies captured Fokker's technology when the pilot of one of his E-1 monoplanes lost his way in fog and mistakenly landed behind our lines. The pendulum of air superiority swung back to the middle.

Despite the imperative of the job, there remained a code of conduct between aerial adversaries which afforded a mutual respect to one another. The parents of one British lieutenant, who had been shot down, learned of their son's fate via his victors. Having landed safely behind enemy lines, he was captured, treated courteously, dined well in their squadron mess, and then given pen and paper to write to his parents to assure them that he was safe. Next day, the letter was dropped over his own squadron airfield for onward transmission to his home.

Whilst the Luftstreitkräfte had for a time enjoyed the aerial advantage of the secret synchronised machine gun, in September the following year it was Britain's turn to hold the advantage. The start of the battle of Flers-Courcelette on the 15th of that month saw the debut of our own secret weapon, the tank. Haig was at the time, and has been since, heavily criticised for using them in such small numbers during the battle, rather than awaiting their greater availability and the benefit of refined reliability. Of the forty-nine tanks sent over to the Somme, thirty-two began the attack, of which only nine reached the German lines. Whilst the impact on the Kaiser's infantry was undoubted, it was minimal outside the immediate point of contact, whereas greater numbers would have considerably multiplied the effect.

That said, Rawlinson was very pleased with the way those tanks that had made it through performed. Our troops made substantial advances during the day along a six-mile front to a depth of between two and three thousand yards. Martinpuich, High Wood, Flers and Courcelette were all taken.

In Britain, the impact of the war on the civilian population was perceptibly incremental. At first, there was, as so often, great confidence that it would all be over by Christmas; that the army and the navy would sort out the Kaiser and that would be the end of it. In the early months, civilians, isolated from the reality of the fighting, were generally either energetically enthusiastic about the whole affair or largely disinterested. It was only those families who were directly affected by the deaths or injuries suffered by their menfolk that the war touched. Not for almost a thousand years had the civilian population of these islands been put to the sword by an enemy as they lay in their beds. The shelling of Yarmouth, Scarborough, Hartlepool and Whitby just before that first Christmas stunned the nation into the realisation that the German invasion of France would not be quickly resolved.

Within little more than a month, East Anglia was once more the target when two Zeppelins, diverted from their attack on Hull by bad weather, dropped their bombs on Great Yarmouth, Sheringham, King's Lynn and the surrounding villages during the night of 19th/20th January 1915, killing four people and injuring sixteen more. Death and destruction had been visited upon them unseen and unheard. The concept of 'total war' had not yet been formulated and there was widespread public alarm and disgust at this new form of warfare that, by irresistible implication, targeted women and children as they slept. The net of civilian involvement was being cast wider as each month passed.

At first, the Kaiser refused to authorise attacks on London for fear of injuring his royal cousins, but on 12th February he signed an Imperial Order which permitted the bombing of the docks, which his military staff interpreted as anything in the East End. Zeppelins, though, were fragile machines. Restricted to conditions of little or no wind, they were always at the mercy of the weather. Most of the early raids were either aborted or ended badly for the crews. One airship taking part in a raid on England in October was blown so far off course it was last seen out of control and heading out over the Mediterranean! In April, the new P-class ships were delivered and the LZ38, commanded by Hauptman Erich Linnarz, carried out the first bombing raid on London during the night of 30th/31st May.

In total, Zeppelins, together with the Schütte-Lanz airships, carried out twenty raids over Britain in 1915. The losses the following year, however, resulted in the Imperial Army Fleet being withdrawn, although attacks from the German navy fleet on targets in England and Scotland continued. During the year, the RFC and the RNAS were equipped with the new incendiary machine-gun bullets, and coupled with new aeroplane designs which achieved a greater rate of climb and a higher ceiling, their pilots exacted a heavy penalty upon the remaining airship force. 31st July 1916 saw the L-31 under the command of the highly experienced Kapitänleutnant Heinrich Mathy almost shot out of the sky by the gunners of HMTB 117 which was patrolling the Thames estuary. The resultant damage to the L-31 was such that it was forced to abandon its mission and return home. The captain of HMTB 117 that day was Lieutenant Charles Lightoller, the former Second Officer aboard the *Titanic*; he was awarded the Distinguished Service Cross for this action.

Mathy's fifteenth and final mission was on the night of 1st/2nd October, when the L-31 was shot down at 15,000 feet in dramatic circumstances by 2nd Lieut. Wulstan Tempest flying his 39 Squadron BEc2 4577 from Suttons Farm. The encounter led to Tempest being awarded the Distinguished Service Order.

By 1917, the Zeppelin force was spent. Its impact upon civilian morale overall had been marginal, it had lost the propaganda war having been labelled a 'baby-killer' and it had consumed disproportionate resources of men and materials at a time when Germany could no longer afford the losses. Although occasional raids occurred into 1917, it was gradually replaced by fixed-wing bombers, mainly the Gotha. Nevertheless, the bombing campaign was not without its strategic gains for the Kaiser's forces. The main effect, principally consequent upon the bombing of London, was that Haig was forced to release some of his front-line squadrons in France to help protect the Home skies and the capital in particular.

There was an unseen consequence for the British too, although it would be another twenty-two years before the immensity of its impact would be witnessed. The RFC and the RNAS had differing roles in the war; in short, the RFC saw its function as supporting the army of which it was a part. The RNAS, likewise, saw its function to support the navy. In 1917, the War Cabinet realised that a co-ordinated defence force was necessary to protect Britain's skies and invited one of its members, the South African Boer leader General Smuts, to write a report reviewing the air services. In this task he was greatly supported by the RFC's commander, Lieutenant-General Sir David Henderson, who wrote most of the report. The son of a Glasgow ship-building family, Henderson had entered university at fifteen where he had read engineering before being commissioned into the Argyll and Sutherland Highlanders. In 1911 he learned to fly, becoming, at the age of forty-nine, the world's oldest pilot at that time.

The report recommended the creation of an independent air force by the amalgamation of the RFC and RNAS. On 1st April 1918 the Royal Air Force came into being, creating the world's first, largest and most powerful independent air force, with over 20,000 aircraft and 300,000 personnel. However, in the early autumn of 1916, as I watched the aerial trials of skill and endurance played out far above me, all this was as unknown to me as it was to those young aviators. Everyone at the Front was the same; we took each day, and sometimes each hour, as it came. Tomorrow was too far ahead to think about.

For the RE, our daily routine of maintenance work continued along the trenches and back towards Béthune, wherever there were cables laid and men and shells to break them. It rained to a greater or lesser extent almost every day that autumn, and we were issued with thigh-length gumboots whenever we were in the Cuinchy/Cambrin trenches. Although these boots were a real godsend for keeping our feet dry, they did make moving about in the mud more difficult, but that was the lesser of the two evils. The temperatures were beginning to fall as the winter approached, and 9th November saw the first night frosts coating the wet surfaces with a crystal glaze and reddening the noses of the men at the dawn stand-to. By the end of the year, it was clear that this winter was going to be a particularly hard one.

With the passing of each day, the cold became more intense. The ground became so hard that it was no longer possible to dig it out to repair the parapets. In their trenches a few yards away, the Germans were suffering just as much as we were, and whilst I would not pretend any friendship between us, there was a certain recognition of mutual misery. With the opposing lines being so close to one another, there were guarded conversations about the conditions shouted across No Man's Land. Even the shelling was reduced at times as each side's artillery struggled with frozen gun mechanisms. We had a common enemy, the searing cold.

Even though life was much harder then than it is now and we were much tougher, these conditions were unprecedented and to have to suffer them in the trenches of the Western Front was almost beyond endurance. Fingers were always numb with cold, which made handling weapons, tools, food, drink, anything, a clumsy affair, and not without its dangers. Feet had long since lost any feeling. The unrelenting freezing air turned everything it touched to a solid mass, and if that happened to be a soldier's wet feet frostbite quickly set in, but without the sense of feeling there was no pain; that would come later out of the line, as the body began to thaw. We were told not to remove our boots, but I did at night. Our officer had got hold of some whale oil for us and we shared it around the team.

There was no escape from that cold; that's what made it so unbearable, the relentlessness of it. We were all living outside, in trenches, in dugouts, in broken buildings. Even those troops pulled back into the rest areas had little or no heating provided in their huts, and some were even resting in tents. When the sun shone, it teased us with the promise of spring and the gift of warmth, but its perfidious rays held no heat to share with us.

Increasingly, the infantry men being sent to the sector were little more than boys, many having lied about their age to join Kitchener's New Army. Looking at some of them made me feel old. I saw some of these boys openly cry with the hardship of it all. The misery of never being warm, of trying to clean a rifle knowing that your skin would stick to the metal if you touched it without gloves, trying to melt ice with a candle and quickly shave before the water froze again, going for days on end without a hot meal or mug of tea, having to suck ice because there was no liquid water; it nearly brought us all to our knees. Hot food, usually a meat and potato stew washed down with tea, was prepared in field kitchens which were generally set up about a thousand yards behind the front line. Once ready, it was put into large metal containers which were then wrapped in a woollen jacket to keep the contents hot. After dark, each company would send men to fetch the supplies, all of which had to be carried along the communication trenches to their comrades at the front. Even with duckboards down, the going was slow and hard. Water, mud, ice, shellfire, stretcher bearers, other supply-carrying soldiers, all made progress tedious, and in the bitter temperatures nothing was even vaguely warm by the time it reached the waiting men. The only thing that didn't freeze was the rum ration, often issued morning and night during that winter. For days and nights at a time in the line, it was the only warmth we had.

If it was bad for us, it was worse for the Scottish Regiments, who all wore kilts. At least we wore trousers, but even these men, much more used to the cold, had to wrap their bare legs in field bandages to prevent the frost and the ice crystals which formed on their kilts and stiffened the heavy wool from cutting into their flesh as they moved about.

Like everyone else, I wore as many clothes as I could. My sisters had been knitting me extra pairs of socks ever since my first bout of trench foot and, with the approach of winter, had sent me a woollen jersey, scarf and gloves. Almost all the men had someone at home who would knit them warm clothing and those that didn't would be given something by a mate or from the many life-saving Red Cross parcels which arrived in a steady stream. In the front line, there was a very relaxed attitude about what was worn underneath our uniforms in order to keep warm and dry. I wore regulation woollen long-johns underwear, a woollen shirt, then a jersey, cardigan or pullover, then the SD tunic and finally my double-breasted coat on the top. This double-breasted version was issued to mounted troops and proved to be a real godsend to me during that winter. Underneath my steel helmet I wore a balaclava with a scarf around my neck and two pairs of gloves. Despite all these clothes, I still felt the cold and desperately wanted my moose-skin coat again.

The bitter cold did, though, bring some unexpected relief. The smell from decomposing bodies and rancid mud that hung over the lines had faded, frozen into animated suspension. The air might have remained full of cordite, but it felt good to breathe. The other relief was from the rats. Their main food source was now deep frozen in that suspended animation, and as the cold took its toll on their numbers we gladly threw their lifeless petrified forms into No Man's Land. Plunderers of our food, ravagers of our belongings, despoilers of our bodies, we cradled no affection for them but took delight in the knowledge that they, who uninvited had chosen to share this miserable godforsaken desolation with us, now shared our suffering too.

On Christmas Eve 1916, the 1st Battalion Bedfordshire Regiment came into the line at Cuinchy and relieved the 16th Royal Warwickshires, who moved back to the support trench. That night found me repairing a wire at the Cabbage Patch Redoubt, which was in the care of 'C' Company, the Bedfords. The intense cold had made the wires brittle and as ice bore down on them, breakages were common. I struggled with the delicate work through gloved fingers. At last the connection was restored and I stepped back to look up for a moment into the vastness of the heavens. Had we not been where we were, it would have been a night to behold. A shooting star fled across the sky beneath the brilliant, shimmering pinpoints of celestial light that shone and danced through air that was as clear and sharp as crystal. Here on earth, the ground was like iron; condensed breath froze instantly on men's moustaches and clothes. A strange uneasy unfamiliar stillness descended over the battlefield. Sentries were posted as usual but no patrols were out.

Then, as midnight approached, quietly at first, the strains of a lone voice drifted on that stillness across the Slough of Despond that lay between us: *Stille Nacht, heilige Nacht, Alles schläft; einsam wacht Nur das traute hochheilige Paar.* Gradually, his fellows joined him in all six verses, and as the hymn reached the ascendant message of Peace in its final couplet, for those of us there that night it held a particular poignancy. It had been so beautifully and movingly sung that it was hard to remember that the choir was our enemy. I had simply stood and listened with a lump in my throat. I knew that my parents would at that moment be in Cressage church for the midnight service, perhaps singing the same hymn.

Then across the divide came in accented tones, "Hey, Tommy. Merry Christmas to you."
"And to you too, Fritz. Sing us another one," somebody called back.

But it was not to be. It was as if Generals Haig and Hindenburg had heard the singing and ordered both sets of artillery simultaneously to begin a bombardment, albeit somewhat intermittent and rather half-hearted. There would be no more carols that night. Orders had been sent down that there was to be no fraternisation with the enemy; both our own and the German commanders did not want a repeat of the 1914 Christmas truce. They saw such events as being bad for morale. Truces, though, did happen all the time along the Western Front. Usually it was in order to recover the wounded and dead by both sides after particularly fierce fighting. At other times they simply happened by silent acquiescence arising from sheer exhaustion; an unofficial acceptance that each side would emerge in daylight to repair their defences. Inevitably, these were very localised and, almost by definition, occurred in areas where snipers were not active.

The narrow strip of ground between the two sides in the Cuinchy sector was no longer recognisable as the place of soft, gently undulating fields it had once been. As far as we could see left and right, it was just a haphazard jumble of craters, tree stumps, troughs and heaps of shattered landscape. Water or ice filled every dip, hollow and hole.

The icy weather was to deliver yet another dimension of danger to our already overburdened daily lives. The ground had frozen so hard that some of the lighter shells couldn't penetrate it and so exploded on immediate surface impact, exacerbating the spread of shrapnel. Even the small cushioning effect of the soft ground was denied to us. Other shells simply hit the ice and ricocheted off, bouncing once or twice like skimming stones before exploding. However, for one young officer this at least proved to be providential. The shell struck the ground four feet to one side and slightly behind him, bounced and exploded 150 yards in front. The gunner had seemingly misspelled his name on that one.

After Christmas it snowed. It should have felt warmer but it didn't. Frostbite cases increased as the snow seeped into puttees, wetted trousers, socks, boots and feet. The snow fell for days on end. In the trenches it was trodden into gravy-coloured slush, which made moving about even more difficult. In No Man's Land, it tried its best to cover the despoiled ground of shell holes, tree stumps and mounds of erupted earth. Had the artillery let it, the white mantle would have succeeded in hiding the evidence of our hideous activities, but the guns persisted and the earth continued to spew forth ingested bodies, relics and detritus.

Perhaps the warmest job on the Front was that carried out by the tunnelling companies because they were underground. In the early months of the trench war, the Cuinchy/Cambrin sector was the scene of ten small but effective underground mines which were exploded beneath our lines on 21st December 1914. We had no tunnelling force at the time but, uncharacteristically, the military acted very quickly and by March the following year, under the umbrella of the RE, tunnelling companies of experienced miners from all over Britain had been formed and were working along the Front.

The first tunnelling companies were brought out by Major John Norton-Griffiths. From an unprivileged background and something of a rebel, Norton-Griffiths wasted the education his clerk of works father had tried to provide for him. In 1887, he served a year with the Life Guards before joining the British South Africa Police at the time of the Second Matabele War in 1896. This led to service in the Second Boer War, where he rose to the rank of Captain Adjutant to Lord Roberts' bodyguard. Rough and tough, in the intervening years he had trained to be a civil engineer and it was he who introduced the clay-kicking mining method to the British Army in early 1915 when a solution to combat German subterranean warfare was desperately needed.

The clay of northern France and Belgium greatly favoured this tunnelling method, which entailed a man sitting down and leaning against his mate's back in a tunnel only four to five feet high and three feet wide whilst pressing the shovel into the clay with his foot. The alternative method was to hack the clay with a mattock. The clay-kicking method gave us a number of advantages; it was quick, moving a tunnel forward at the rate of over twenty-six feet a day, it was virtually silent and it was unknown to the Germans, who used the slower and noisier mattock method, which drove a tunnel at around six feet per day. As a result, it was much easier for us to hear them at work than for them to hear us, and because it was much quicker, we were able to blow their trenches more often than they ours.

The methods of Norton-Griffiths, now a major in the RE, greatly inspired and influenced the Engineer-in-Chief of the BEF, Brigadier George Fowke, who it was, in September 1915, that devised the strategy of a deep mining offensive. Norton-Griffiths, known as 'Empire Jack', was awarded the DSO and made lieutenant-colonel in 1916. He was the grandfather of Liberal politician Jeremy Thorpe.

We had No.251 Tunnelling Company with us at Cuinchy. They had arrived in October 1915, when they took over from the No.170 TC, and remained until the Allied advance in the final offensive of summer 1918. 251 TC were also responsible for detonating the final British mine of the war on 10th August 1917 near Givenchy-en-Gohelle, north of Arras. The miners worked by sinking a central shaft from which they struck out with tunnels in different directions towards the enemy's lines. At the end of the gallery a small sap only about three feet high and wide was dug for a man to sit in and listen for sounds of the enemy digging. If he could hear them, a camouflet would be used to destroy their tunnel and any miners in it. We stole a year or more of advance upon the Germans with our mining techniques and equipment, a year which they never caught up.

Whilst most mine detonations during the war were relatively modest or were camouflets as part of the quite separate unseen battle which was waged sixty feet below the ground between men who seemed to inhabit a different world altogether, there were some notably immense explosions. One was the massive mine detonated at La Boiselle at 7.28am on 1st July 1916 to signal the start of the Somme battle and which created Lochnagar, the largest man-made crater of the war. Another was at Messines Ridge in western Flanders, where at 3.10am on 7th June 1917, the combined explosive power of nineteen mines created the greatest non-volcanic, non-nuclear blast the planet has ever seen. The sound waves travelled to the Scottish borders, the Swiss recorded it on a seismograph and David Lloyd George maintained that he clearly heard it in London, 150 miles away. They all stand testament to the outstanding courage and ingenuity of the men of the tunnelling companies, though none more so than William Hackett, VC of No.254 TC.

Courage is an indefinable quality. It cannot be measured, for courage is what is brought by the individual; it is what makes people do not only exceptional acts but also ordinary acts in exceptional circumstances. There are many people who are not natural heroes and yet, cometh the hour, cometh the man or the woman. Sometimes courage is born in the intensity of battle, sometimes in the impossibility of the situation, sometimes in the plight of others. Courage can be fuelled by adrenalin, by duty, friendship, love or compassion, and these can be seen and understood. But occasionally, there occurs an act of cold, calculated courage and supreme sacrifice which surpasses all and defies normal rules of comprehension. On 22nd June 1916, Sapper William Hackett committed such an act.

In the early hours of that day, the forty-three-year-old Hackett and four others of 254 TC were working thirty-five feet below No Man's Land near Givenchy, driving a tunnel 4 feet 3 inches high and 2 feet 6 inches wide, when the Germans exploded a mine which collapsed twenty feet of the tunnel, trapping the five men. A rescue was started and after twenty hours the men were reached. Hackett helped three to safety through the narrow escape hole, but the fourth, Thomas Collins, was seriously wounded and unable to be brought through the hole. The earth was beginning to slide in, closing the passage, and the rescuers knew that there would not be time to widen the hole and rescue Collins before continued German shelling collapsed the tunnel again.

Although uninjured and with safety beckoning, Hackett, long overdue home leave to return to his wife and family, refused to leave the injured Collins to die alone in the dark, knowing that to stay with him meant certain death. The rescuers continued in their efforts but eventually the tunnel collapsed under the weight of enemy fire. For another four days their comrades desperately dug to reach the men but finally had to recognise defeat. The two men remain where they died, in that dark tunnel deep under the French countryside. Hackett was awarded a posthumous Victoria Cross, one of only two men from the tunnelling companies to be so honoured during the war, although his alone was for action underground. His medals are now held by the RE Museum at Chatham.

Many was the time that I would see the men of the 251 TC heading through the trenches towards the shaft. I just could not imagine what it would be like crawling along these small tunnels knowing that at any moment the enemy might blow them in, trapping them down there. I suppose the trouble was, I could imagine it and it filled me with terror. I would say to them that I didn't know how they did it. Their reply was always the same; they didn't know how I did my job because they considered it much safer underground than on the top amongst the shells and the snipers and the cold and the mud. Statistically, of course, they were right, but I could not have changed places with them for anything. My great dread was that the officer would order me to run a telephone cable down into those tunnels.

The Menin Gate, Ypres

I sent this postcard to Violet. It was typical of picture cards at the time.

This is a Christmas card that I sent to Violet.
It was made by one of the local girls.

Chapter Fourteen

"I, too, saw God through mud, -
The mud that cracked on cheeks when wretches smiled.
War brought more glory to their eyes than blood,
And gave their laughs more glee than shakes a child."
Apologia Pro Poemate Meo – Lt. Wilfred Owen, MC

Tell the last man in the line to close the Menin Gate. By 1917, this was the soldiers' joke as they marched through the gap in the ramparts where the Menin Gate had once stood. From October 1914, nearly every British and Commonwealth soldier who fought on the Ypres section of the Western Front passed along this road and through the gate; hence the joke.

Until early 1917, America had no desire, political will or popular support to join the great pan-European war that had so paralysed us. Even when it did, it was out of self-serving interest rather than any altruistic motive. US President Woodrow Wilson had maintained the army at peacetime levels, had no air force to speak of and had only marginally expanded his navy in order to protect the American home waters of the eastern seaboard. Although Congress made financial loans to Britain and France, Wilson made strenuous efforts to maintain his country's neutrality. In particular, he insisted that the belligerents did not interfere with American shipping and trade.

Germany, though, was its own worst enemy in the fight for the hearts and minds of US citizens. News of the atrocities committed against Belgian civilians by advancing troops, followed by the sinking of the Cunard passenger liner *Lusitania* on 7th May 1915 at the hands of the U-20, causing the deaths of 128 American passengers, all helped with Britain's propaganda cause.

By 1916, the Royal Navy's blockade of German ports was having a significant impact upon the enemy's ability to sustain its war effort in France and Russia, and its population at home were beginning to experience serious shortages. To enforce the blockade, the navy impounded or turned back neutral ships, including American vessels. Wilson protested these violations of neutrality to the British government and the navy was ordered to no longer impede American vessels heading for Germany. Nevertheless, the blockade continued to bite as the war progressed and, in its desperate need for soldiers, Germany drew farmers from the land. With an insufficient agricultural workforce, its stocks of food supplies became seriously threatened.

Knowing what was coming and in anticipation of war with the United States, in mid January 1917, Germany's Foreign Minister Arthur Zimmermann sent a telegram to his country's Ambassador to Mexico, Heinrich von Eckardt. The message proposed that if the Americans entered the war an alliance should be formed between Mexico and Germany, the purpose of which would be for Germany to financially support and facilitate a Mexican invasion of America designed to regain the states of New Mexico, Arizona and Texas. To avoid interception, the telegram was sent from Berlin to the German embassy in Washington from where it was transmitted to von Eckardt. It was on this last leg that British Intelligence in Room 40 at the Admiralty Building intercepted and decoded the message. Having verified the veracity of the message, its contents were disclosed to the American president.

At about the same time, in a move designed as a retaliation against the blockade but in the knowledge that sooner or later it would lead to war with the United States, von Hindenburg and Ludendorff, now joint heads of the Imperial military, committed Germany's U-boat force to unconditional warfare against all shipping sailing in the Atlantic war zone and British waters. It was a decision whose consequences would reach far beyond the Great

War and would ultimately shape world politics for generations to come. What they did not foresee, and could not have foreseen, was that it would, within thirty years, directly lead to America becoming the most powerful nation on earth.

Wilson had come to recognise that the balance of world power in the post-Victorian age was going to be settled on the battlefields of Europe and he did not want America to be isolated from it. Until then, the United States, having shed its colonial shackles, had largely focussed upon becoming a great trading nation, leaving the imperialistic nations of Europe to resolve their differences as they had always done. Now, though, he saw the threat to America's avowed desire to spread democracy, liberalism and independence across the globe. If Germany won it would dominate Europe and that would allow it to extend its unwelcome Teutonic influence to the southern neighbours: Latin America. The Zimmermann telegram was all the proof of that proposition that he needed. If the British and French won, they would carve up the world without taking into account any of America's interests. It had become a national imperative that the United States entered the war on the side of the Allies. His assessment not only gained him wide support at the time but has shaped and guided American foreign policy ever since. It was this latter consequence that von Hindenburg and Ludendorff could not have foreseen.

Then, in March, five US merchant ships were torpedoed in quick succession. The American public were outraged and, amidst a growing sense of national assertion, the mood of the country changed. Wilson released the telegram and opposition to the war largely melted away. The public swung behind Wilson, who knew that not only could he no longer defend America's neutrality, but that it would be against his country's best interests. He now sought what he described to Congress as "a war to end war".

On 6th April, Congress approved a declaration of war against Germany, and the following day, against Austro-Hungary. In the House of Representatives, Jeanette Rankin was one of fifty who voted against America's entry into the war. In 1941, after Pearl Harbor, she again voted against war, but that time she was a lone voice in her opposition.

One of the hardest facets of life at the Front was the constant exposure to artillery fire. There were long periods of relentless noise from shells passing overhead and of the shock waves reverberating through the air from explosions that not only ripped the land apart but battered the body. Men were shouting, others crying and calling out for stretcher bearers amid the fear and destruction of the whizz-bangs, *minenwerfers* and trench mortars that landed amongst us, sending stiletto pieces of shrapnel scything the air. If it wasn't the roar of their guns close to the lines, it was ours, and if it wasn't our short-range howitzers, it was their long-range artillery or it was ours, or both. Then, if it was quiet where we were, we could hear the next sector or some distant one under fire. It was the sheer relentlessness of the noise some days that became so hard to bear.

It wasn't that the guns were firing continuously, they weren't but they did at some point nearly every day and it became increasingly hard to bear as each month passed. There were times, though, when nothing whizzed, banged, whooshed, whined, sweed, boomed or cracked. Sometimes two or three days would pass without any exchanges, although this brought the danger of complacency, which was just when the sniper would strike. However, these were also days and nights when repairs to trenches, defences and wiring could be carried out much more easily.

The war had produced an escalation in the capacity and calibre of artillery weapons and with it what seemed to be an exponential desire by commanders to exploit that capability to its fullest. The immense bombardment which presaged the Battle of Arras had started on 20th March, and our gunners fired 2,689,000 shells along a twenty-four-mile front. To put that into some context, it was a million more shells than we had fired nine months earlier to start the Somme.

Good Friday, 6th April. That deep, iron-hard cold which had marked the winter was reluctant to morph into springtime. Two days later, beneath clear skies in a bitter wind that blew off the North Sea, swept across the plains and cut straight through us, I joined the congregation for the Easter Sunday service and communion. Our efforts at hymn singing were all but drowned by the thunderous roar of the guns. The noise and the bitingly cold wind did, however, persuade the padre to reduce the service to its bare essentials and his sermon to a minimum few words. The Lord does indeed move in mysterious ways! After the service, I returned to my billet and packed my kit ready for my next spell at the Front.

The northern flank of the attack stopped barely three miles south of us, but the guns of our sector added to the barrage to once more deter the enemy from moving men and guns south into the battle zone. That Sunday night as I moved forward to Cuinchy, the firing eased and with it came some relief from the continuous rumble and thunder of the guns that had obliterated all other sounds for three weeks. The attack had been planned for Easter Sunday but, despite the clear weather, it had been put back until the following day at the request of the French. In the early hours of Easter Monday, 9th April 1917, the wind strengthened and it began to snow heavily.

Just before the 5.30am start, there was a frenzied artillery bombardment, the like of which we had never heard before. For five minutes, every gun we had along that front between us and St

Quentin was firing at maximum speed. The flashes and clamour completely engulfed us. They were deafening, painful, spectacular, wondrous, uplifting; even by the perverse standards of the Western Front, this was both impressive and unprecedented. Then, the hurricane of shells stopped as suddenly as it had started and transformed into a creeping barrage under which, as the whistles blew, our men advanced upon an enemy unaware and stupefied into total shock.

In driving snow, the British advanced upon Observation Ridge whilst the First Army Canadian Corps of Lieutenant-General Sir Julian Byng attacked Vimy Ridge. In both assaults, the defending troops were caught unawares as the snow which blew on the backs of our infantry blew into the eyes of the defenders; they never saw us coming. The capture of the high ground was critical to the whole Arras operation, as the ridges, and Vimy in particular, were the highest parts of the area and dominated the Douai plain, the coalfields of Lens and the wider German positions. The success of the operation, and particularly the rapid capture of Vimy Ridge, was largely due to Byng's meticulous planning together with the innovative use of tactics including the intensive training of his troops, a heavy use of machine guns, clearly defined objectives and the division of companies into four platoons at least one of which had a Lewis gun.

In the air, the Royal Flying Corps, despite suffering the considerable loss of 131 aircraft during the first week of April at the hands of von Richthofen's experienced and well-equipped JG1 Flying Circus, managed to maintain and fulfil its role as observer above the German positions and to keep the First and Third Army commanders fully informed of progress, artillery shell falls and enemy movements. More importantly, though, the RFC crews had been able to locate hidden German guns from their muzzle flashes and relay this detail back to the 1st Field Survey Company of the RE. By correlating the flash-spotting and sound-ranging information being fed to them, the RE had been able to calculate the exact position of the enemy's guns. By the start of the battle, 80% of these weapons had been completely destroyed or put out of use. Half the casualties of the Somme had been caused by German artillery fire into troops crossing No Man's Land or waiting in our trenches. It was one of the many lessons taken from the Somme.

Little by little, the enemy was pushed back and we consolidated our positions. Although the Canadians had secured the main area of Vimy Ridge, the south-east flank near Arleux-en-Gohelle east of Arras remained in enemy hands. The Arleux Loop, as it was known, was a salient in the German lines from where they could mount a counter-attack to Vimy Ridge. It had to be taken to maintain the push forwards. On 28th April, the bitter fight for the loop began. The attacking forces included the Highland Light Infantry, which, as part of the Childers Reforms of the army, had been formed in 1881 from the amalgamation of the 71st and 74th (Highland) Regiments of Foot, becoming the 1st and 2nd Battalions HLI, respectively.

Private George Ballantyne was part of the 2nd Battalion which, at 4.25am that pitch-dark morning, began to move forward against the enemy positions under difficult and trying navigation conditions. As the attack began, they were met by fierce opposition. A counter-barrage, lethal machine gunning and accurate shellfire all took a dreadful toll upon the advancing HLI. The fighting lasted throughout that day and through the next. For George, however, there would be no tomorrow. At some point during the first day, the twenty-three-year-old was caught by the full blast of a shell from a field gun.

Some ten days later, the postie walked slowly down Thornhill Street, Parkhead. He knew the people here well, for he was one of them. The people who stayed in this part of Glasgow did not often receive official letters, and if they did it was generally bad news.

That day his delivery bag weighed more heavily than ever before, even though its contents were few. He had refused to let telegraph boys deliver the fateful messages. George's home at No.32, within sight of Celtic Park football ground, was one in a row of typical Glasgow east-end tenements which lined each side of the streets in this and most of the city's poor neighbourhoods. The once sturdy red sandstone buildings, now long since demolished, housed twelve families each. The young soldier's parents, George and Jane Crawford Ballantyne, had been so proud to see their son join the HLI at the end of July 1913. It had offered him an escape from the deprivation, the reekin', dense, smoke-laden, toxic air and the grim relentlessness of Glasgow's poverty that was as much a part of the city in those days as was its great industrial wealth and cultural influence that led the world.

George had been in France since the beginning of the war. He had survived Mons, the Marne, the Aisne and First Ypres in 1914, Festubert and Loos in 1915, Delville Wood on the Somme and Ancre in 1916, and First and Second Scarpe earlier in April 1917. Finally, his luck had run out. George Ballantyne still lies somewhere near Arleux, lost amongst the folds of French soil, far from his native Scotland; but he is still remembered by the Flowers of the Forest and by his name engraved on Bay 8 of the Arras Memorial.

By the early summer, my brother Herbert had finished his training as a signaller with the Welch Regiment and had been posted out to join me in this miserable existence. I had news of him, and he of me, via our letters home to Mother. We each told her as much as we could or were allowed and she relayed this on to the other one. Herbert was with the 15th Battalion, 114th Brigade, 38th Division of the Regiment. The Division had last seen action at Mametz Wood on the Somme, where they had taken such appalling casualties that it was more than twelve months before it was back in the line.

Fortunately, Herbert had not been at Mametz, but now he waited with the 15th Battalion at Ypres, where they would open the Third Battle with an attack on Pilckem Ridge; strategically, the Western Front was all about the ridges.

After the Arras offensive and the collapse of the French attack at Chemin de Dames, which their commander General Robert Nivelle had believed would end the war in forty-eight hours, the line to our south settled back to the stalemate which had gripped it for so long. Elsewhere, we had moved forward a few miles and straightened our lines; the Germans had fallen back a few miles to prepared positions on the Hindenburg line, and straightened theirs. There were mutinies in the French army and we were stretched even further to fill the gaps and prevent the Germans finding out that an opportunity for victory existed. To take the pressure off the new French commander, General Philippe Pétain, it was decided to launch a new offensive in Flanders to try and break out of the Ypres salient.

Twenty miles to our north, the 7th June saw the start, with the series of Messines Ridge explosions followed by an infantry assault. Senior German officers had failed to heed warnings from their field commanders that our miners were busy. Within a week, the enemy had withdrawn his front line from the Wyteschaete Ridge, but the follow-up attack did not get under way for another seven weeks. It was preceded in mid June by another immense bombardment when 3,000 Allied guns fired 4,250,000 artillery shells along an eleven-mile front.

In addition to relieving pressure on the French army during their mutiny period, there were quite distinct and legitimate military aims for Third Ypres, including the capture of Roulers, a rail centre vital to the German control of Flanders, and the seizing of the Belgian coast.

As at Arras, the huge opening bombardment was concluded in the last few minutes by a massive hurricane of shells. Even at Cuinchy, the air had reverberated to the thunderous roar of the bombardment, and in the early hours we had felt the increase in pace of firing and knew that the moment had come. I whispered a prayer for my brother.

The bombardment, which surpassed that at Arras and dwarfed the prelude to the Somme, gave notice to the German Fourth Army that we were coming. On 31st July we came, and so did the rain; and it rained almost every day in August. During that month, more than five inches of rain fell in northern France and Flanders, but it was not just wet, it was blown in on a storm which lasted for five days. It was not supposed to rain like that during August. In 1914, in the days before the war started, the weather was beautiful; the people of France danced in the parks to the music from the bandstands, and yet throughout the war, the weather was consistently wetter and colder than normal.

At 3.50am the whistles blew and Herbert went over the top with the 15th, following behind the creeping barrage across a battlefield lit by bursting shells and flares. The attack at Pilckem Ridge was the opening phase of Third Ypres and progress against the enemy was swift and decisive. By lunchtime it had started to drizzle; by late afternoon the drizzle had turned to heavy rain and the ground, churned and ruptured by two weeks of incessant shelling, became an impassable quagmire. The attacks along the front faltered and then halted.

It was that unremitting rain during August, October and November, embracing the struggle for Passchendaele, which produced the sea of mud over the battlefield and through which progress of any sort was both painfully slow and arduous. It is Passchendaele's satanic imagery of desolation, mud, misery, hardship and horror; of horses and men slowly drowning in the endless swamp of stinking, semolina-filled craters, which has come down through history to represent the abomination and tragedy of the Western Front in the minds of the public.

As a result of our local artillery keeping the pressure on the Germans in the Cuinchy sector during the Arras campaign, we had taken quite a battering in return. Our small band of REs had lost five men to shellfire; three whilst working in the trenches and the other two caught in the open to the rear of Cambrin. Fortunately, all five survived. Three were lucky enough to have caught a 'Blighty' and be sent back to England for treatment and recovery. We were now short, though, and had to work almost without rest for days to keep the telephone wires repaired and working, especially in the forward positions.

Like everyone, I was exhausted and increasingly cold from being soaked to the skin for days at a time. There were occasions when I could hardly focus on the slim connections for the pain in my eyes from lack of sleep. Over those cold days and nights I think the only thing that kept us going was the double rum ration. The Cuinchy water table overflowed. All through August we were never less than knee deep in filthy, stinking, putrid water, often wading waist-deep through some sections. Dugouts were flooded, trenches collapsed, telephone lines became lost, communications struggled, but the rats still flourished, swimming, scrambling, burrowing; ever present. The collapse of the trenches was the most serious and it was a losing battle that we all fought to try to repair them with liquid soil. Our only consolation once more was that the enemy were suffering the same hardships and problems. Particularly adverse weather conditions tended to bring about a reduction in firing across the divide as both sides became preoccupied with the conditions.

Our cellar filled with water and we were forced out to find new accommodation, which we eventually did in a badly shelled house with half a roof. The back portion of the cottage remained fairly watertight and was not at all uncomfortable even if a little cramped. The general conditions were so bad that our officer tried to rotate us more often than usual, but our replacements were not yet experienced enough to work without supervision; there were just not enough of us to go round and so there was little that he could realistically do. However, although it rained just as hard in Béthune, when we did get back there, at least our billet was dry and we had regular hot food from the field kitchen. I continued to suffer with 'trench foot' caused by days of being continuously immersed in the slimy water, but the regular rubbing with whale oil managed to prevent permanent damage.

One of the constant bugbears of being at Béthune was staff inspections. Our own officer inspections were just a part of what we did; it was the staff ones that we resented because the officers expected us to be immaculately presented as if we were still in England. When we were not in the trenches, we were still working rather than resting, as our rest periods were much wider apart than the infantry's, even though we experienced the same conditions in the trenches that they did. As if we didn't have enough to cope with, every so often, our major would tell us that some 'red tab' wanted to inspect us. Some Staff Officers were undoubtedly very good, not just those who had worked their way up and had served in the trenches but also those who had a real understanding and affinity with their men. We had a lot of respect for these officers. Unfortunately, though, there was always the odd one or two who never ventured too far forward, but when they did, they made a bloody nuisance of themselves before going back to the comfort of HQ.

I had never considered myself to be deeply religious but I had been brought up in a Christian household and had maintained my faith throughout my travels. As I looked at the death and destruction that surrounded me, it was very hard to reconcile that faith with the scenes I witnessed, and yet at the same time, that same faith gave me strength and comfort. I carried my small pocket bible with me everywhere and each night I said my prayers whether I was at rest, in a billet or in the trenches.

In September, I received a letter from my friend Iwan to say that he had been badly wounded a few weeks earlier but was now happily recovering. He enclosed a photograph of himself and other casualties from the 6th Canadian Machine Gun Coy convalescing in the sunshine at Seaford in Kent. I was also due a few days' leave and, although it was not long enough for me to get home, it was enough for me to go to Talbot House, universally known as Toc H, at Poperinge. I reported to the local de-lousing centre attached to the bathing station at the colliery in Béthune, where I was able to have a good wash, a proper shave, be issued with a new uniform and have a good hot breakfast before catching the train to Hazebrouck. Two hours later, I changed trains for the short journey into Poperinge, or 'Pops' to all the troops. The railway line went through to Ypres and was an immensely important supply route for the salient. Today, however, the section of track from Poperinge to Hazebrouck no longer exists.

My billet was a bell tent at the rest centre in the Galgebossen, some 230 acres of the old hunting woods belonging to the lords of Elverdinge. We were about a mile to the east of Pops, and whilst well within range of the German guns, the camp was well hidden amongst the trees. I booked in at the orderly room and was given a tent number. When I found it, there was already another chap there, sitting quietly reading. His name was Robert Fernihough, a stretcher bearer who came from Bolton in Lancashire. Fernihough & Co Ltd was an old established family business of grocers, Italian warehousemen and tea dealers whose premises were at 26 Deansgate, telephone number Bolton 64. Its premises sat next to the beautiful building of the Bank of Bolton which, in an early bank acquisition, was taken over by the Manchester and County Bank in 1896. Fernihough's later moved to 56 Deansgate. Before the war, Bob had worked with his father in the business, taking the tram from their home at 58 Manchester Road each morning.

245

Although a more committed Christian than I, Bob was not a conscientious objector although he could have easily applied. He knew that he could not bring himself to kill another human being, but nor could he do nothing, and so he had volunteered for the RAMC, the Royal Army Medical Corps, as a stretcher bearer. It was one of the most dangerous jobs in the line with a very high mortality rate.

It was the role of the unarmed stretcher bearers to follow the attacking troops over the top to give first aid to and, if at all possible, rescue the injured. All this time they were exposed to machine-gun fire, shelling and, in particular, sniper fire, despite wearing clearly marked Red Cross armbands. In between set-piece battles, there was no rest for them in the trenches. They were kept busy night and day as shells and mortars wrought a terrible toll, where accidents were common and where SIWs [self-inflicted wounds] were a fact of life, and death. Night-time patrols might return having had to leave an injured man behind and it was for the bearers to go out and find him, dress his wounds and bring him back to safety, often under the very noses of the enemy.

There were usually two bearers to each stretcher, but in the mud, slime and water-filled shell holes of Flanders and northern France it could often take four men. Their job was dangerous, arduous and unglamorous, wading knee deep through the mud whilst shells and bullets exploded and zipped around them. The stretcher bearer was nobody's friend until he was needed.

Some of the most courageous acts of the war were carried out by these men and it was a stretcher bearer of the North Staffordshire Regiment, Lance Corporal William Coltman, VC, DCM*, MM* from Rangemore near Burton-on-Trent, who would see the Armistice as the most highly decorated NCO and non-combatant of the Great War. He was also Mentioned in Dispatches and awarded the French Croix de Guerre.

Bob had arrived at the camp little more than an hour before me and had come here for one of his regular visits to Toc H. It was still not midday and so we walked back into Pops so that he could show me where to find the club. The town was a hubbub of activity and not for nothing was Pops known to the troops as 'Little Paris'. Shops and estaminet-style cafés, some showing the damage caused by enemy shelling and bombing, ringed the great open space of the oblong central 'square'. All troops going to or coming from the salient passed through that square, along with those who were there on leave and making the most of every moment they had. We watched disinterestedly as a battalion marched through on its way to the Front; outside a café two men argued garrulously, girls offered their services to the limitless market of young and not so young men, whilst singing, beer and laughter bubbled through the windows and around the outside tables.

No.43 of what was then known as Rue de l'Hôpital just off the main square had opened its doors as Talbot House on 11th December 1915 as a very practical memorial to Lieutenant Gilbert WK Talbot of the 7th Battalion The Rifle Brigade, who had been killed at nearby Hooge earlier in the year on 30th July. Established under the guidance of Gilbert's father, the Lord Bishop of Winchester, and his brother Padre Neville Talbot, the purpose of Toc H was to be an Everyman's Club where soldiers could go and relax away from the terrors of the war. The house, and particularly the upper-storey hop loft, had been badly damaged by enemy shelling. The owner, Monsieur Coevoet Camerlynck, had decided that it was too dangerous to remain in Poperinge and had moved his family out of the town. Standing empty, it was the ideal property for the club and was quickly rented by the army for the duration at 150 francs a month. There were a number of conditions attached, one of which was that the army would repair the damage to the building, a job which was of course handed to the Royal Engineers.

After some debate, the building was named Talbot House, which quickly became known simply as Toc H, the signallers' phonetics for its initials, TH. The running of the Club was put into the very capable hands of the Reverend Philip 'Tubby' Clayton, who made it everything that it was and whose legacy it remains today. He created the rare sanctuary where soldiers, airman and even some sailors could read, write letters home, play music, chat and drink endless cups of tea from the ever-simmering urn. All the furnishings, the piano, pictures, books and accessories were donated by grateful servicemen; however, no alcohol and no women were two of the few house rules. Another was no rank. The sign at the door, which still hangs there today, reminded all those entering that, "All rank abandon, ye who enter here." Tubby Clayton is also quoted as saying, "If the army was as well run as the YMCA, we should be home by now." [13 May 1918].

The original hop-drying loft was converted by the soldiers into a chapel, known as the Upper Room. The altar was made from a wooden carpenter's bench found in a shed in the garden and pews were salvaged from ruined churches in the area. The Upper Room became not only a place for services, but also a place of peace for quiet contemplation at any time by anyone.

After the war, M. Camerlynck and his family returned but they became overwhelmed by the numbers of former servicemen who had sheltered and rested within the walls of his house and wanted to see it again. So much so that he resolved to move and in 1929 offered the house for sale. It was bought for £9,200 by Lord Wakefield of Hythe and donated to the Talbot House Association, which remains its owner.

The house was hit by shelling several times during the war without loss of life, but on 28th May 1916, whilst walking in the garden, an unknown Canadian soldier was killed by a high explosive shell. The trials and tribulations of the house itself were not yet over, though, for during World War Two the Germans occupied Ypres and Poperinge, using Toc H as a headquarters and officers' mess. Ironically, this use of the house was a blessing as it protected it from wanton vandalism, although when he requisitioned it, the German commandant was surprised to find it completely bare. As the invaders once more marched over Belgian soil, the house had been stripped of every last vestige of its former use and significance. The entire collection had been secretly removed and divided up amongst the town's residents, never to be seen nor spoken of again during the war. It was as if the contents had never existed. What did exist, however, unbeknown to the new occupiers, was a tunnel under the garden which was part of the network used to spirit away Allied airmen. When Poperinge was liberated in 1944, every last item removed from Toc H was returned in perfect condition.

One quiet day in the mid 1990s, the front doorbell rang, but when answered by the staff, the street outside was empty. On the doorstep was a large black plastic bag. Curious, the staff took the bag in and opened it; what lay inside left them thunderstruck. It was the original wooden cross from Gilbert Talbot's grave, complete with the metal strips, 'LIEUT. G.W.K. TALBOT, 7/ RIFLE BDE, 30-7-15'. Where it had been since 1915 no-one has any idea, but it now hangs to the left of the altar in the Upper Room.

Amongst the thousands of British soldiers who passed through the doors of Toc H during the war, one man stands out; not an armed combatant but an army chaplain, indeed the most highly decorated chaplain of all, Theodore Bayley Hardy, VC, DSO, MC, CF, Chaplain to the King. Although, undoubtedly, some priests remained well behind the lines, that is far from true of a great many of them. In all, five chaplains have been awarded the Victoria Cross, including three in the Great War, and a sixth, Squadron Leader Revd. Herbert C Pugh, was awarded the George Cross in 1941.

Even amongst such illustrious company, Hardy was a remarkable man. Small in stature but immeasurable in presence, before becoming a priest he had been a schoolmaster whose pupils had included DH Lawrence. By the time war came, Hardy was the vicar at St. John's Church, Hutton Roof, near Kirkby Lonsdale in what is now Cumbria, and although then widowed and aged fifty-two, he applied for a post in the army Chaplaincy. After two years of trying, he eventually succeeded and went to France in August 1916. Attached to the 8th Lincolns, he moved up to the Front later that year and never left it. He went over the top at Arras and then at Passchendaele. His decorations came as a result of his unbending commitment to his men in their time of need; when they were wounded and in need of medical care, for carrying stretchers, for staying with them whilst under enemy fire and to comfort them in their last hours.

Space here does not allow more than this short tribute to a remarkable man, but in his interesting biography of Hardy, "*It's Only Me*", David Raw has described the man, his modest nature, his impact upon the men and all who knew him, and his outstanding, quiet courage. Hardy's portrait hangs in the Slessorium at Toc H.

The following day, Bob and I walked through Pops and out towards the west. The autumn had not yet arrived, and here, beyond the range of the guns, the land was alive. Trees were still in their summer greenery, wild flowers nodded and bobbed their delicate, colourful heads in the morning breeze while birds gaily sang from branch and copse, shrub and post. Gone was the sodden monotonous, monochrome fudge brown of endless mud and turned soil; here there was life, peace and hope; there was a semblance of normality.

Later, back in Pops, we visited Toc H again. In the large room at the back of the house overlooking the garden, a young girl sat at the piano and entertained us all with her playing. It seemed surreal that amongst all the carnage, squalor and misery that this war continued to produce, we could sit there and listen to a talented child making beautiful music.

Toc H, which grew into a worldwide movement, provided sanctuary for countless servicemen during the war; Bob and I were no exceptions. The alternative entertainment in the town was generally confined to enjoying the services of the working girls and drinking at the many estaminets which had opened up. Both businesses had increased exponentially to provide for the tens of thousands of troops constantly in the area and in need of the services they offered. During the war, some five million British and Empire troops served on the Western Front and a good proportion of them passed through Poperinge at some time or other.

The need for, and absence of, sex was a problem for many, particularly the older men who were married and had become accustomed to it at home; enforced abstinence made them edgy and irritable. For one middle-aged officer it eventually all became too much and he applied for a week's special leave to Paris. Naturally, the army form required a reason for the request; he simply and honestly wrote, 'sexual starvation.' Much to the delight of his fellow officers, his application was granted and off he went, to return a happier and more focussed leader. Thus did the working girls of Pops, Armentières and elsewhere provide a valued service to those men in such need. Delightful, and indeed necessary though the girls may have been, they were not for everyone and an alternative form of relaxation and escape from the reality of the war was the great gift of Toc H.

There were two undoubted joys for us at Galgebossen; sleep and regular hot food. I also had time to write more than the usual few lines by candlelight to Violet. Although we could hear the guns and occasionally the shells came uncomfortably close, it was bliss to be able to sleep through the night for more than a couple of hours at a time. Utter exhaustion was something that everyone in the front line experienced. The routine of daily duties, the dawn and dusk stand-to, and even the boredom of inactivity in the trenches, coupled with night-time repair work, patrols and enemy shelling, where sleep was snatched in one or two-hour blocks if at all, ground everybody down. Here, I could sleep undisturbed and rest without being called to parade or to line work. The nightmares that would come to haunt me after the war hadn't yet started.

Our meals were prepared in the static cookhouse at the camp and the daily diet that was served up was very good, certainly compared with Maconochie's, and even the cookhouse in Béthune. Here the cooks had access to fresh eggs, good-quality meat and bacon, potatoes, vegetables such as cabbage and turnips; they even served steamed puddings during my stay. Meals were served hot and there was always plenty to eat. The standard of food that the British Army was able to enjoy was something that, as the war dragged on and increasing numbers of German prisoners were taken, they all commented on. They could not believe how good our food was compared with their dwindling rations and deteriorating quality.

I enjoyed my few days' leave, and Bob, with whom I shared many interests and values, had been good company. We had exchanged home addresses together with a promise to meet up again when the whole damnable war was all over. Bob was stationed at nearby Ypres and so set off to walk back to his billet whilst I left Galgebossen in the opposite direction for Pops and the train back to Béthune.

I had been very lucky, for September had been, as so often, wonderfully fine, warm and dry. The surface layers of mud hardened and gave us some relief from the wet. It also provided the opportunity for rebuilding defences and for us, to retrieve and repair cables with a more permanent fix, particularly along the trenches. The dry weather also coincided with the infantry pushes on the Menin Road, Polygon Wood and Broodseinde.

In the last of these actions, on 4th October, the Australians had startling and brilliant success completing their mission by midday, just before the weather broke in the afternoon. Between 4th and 9th another 1¼ inches of rain fell, turning the ground once more into a gooey bog. One consequence of this was that the artillery could not be brought up in support of the infantry; another was that it became immensely arduous to evacuate the wounded. After the war, I met up with Bob again and he told me that it took six and sometimes eight men to carry a stretcher, struggling knee and thigh deep through the morass of sticky, slimy clay mud.

Still it rained. It was now that Field Marshal Haig had to make probably the most difficult decision of his career: to order the continuation to capture the ridge at Passchendaele in these appalling conditions. Although he believed that the Germans were on the point of collapse, he also knew that to halt the attack now would leave his men exposed to counter-attack and annihilation in a position they could not hold, thus losing all the effort and gains that had gone before. Consequently he ordered the attack continue, not knowing that the next six weeks would bring unprecedented rainfall.

Opposing him was Generalfeldmarschall Rupprecht, Crown Prince of Bavaria and commander of the northern armies. On 25th June, the first United States troops had landed in France, and although it would be another year before their presence would be felt in sufficient numbers and training to be effective, the German commander knew that his country's ability to sustain the war, let alone win it, was slipping away. Had Haig been gifted with good weather that late summer and autumn, the much vaunted breakthrough might well have happened. In the event, the weather gods smiled upon the Germans and the Generalfeldmarschall wrote in his diary for 12th October 1917, "*Witterungsumschlag. Erfreulicherweise Regen, unser wirksamster bundesgenosse.*" [Sudden change of weather. Most fortunate rain, our most effective ally.] Despite the hope offered to him by the rain, the Passchendaele ridge was finally taken by the Canadians on 6th November, bringing the Third Battle of Ypres to a close on the 10th without the breakthrough Haig so dearly sought.

Not until after the war did I become aware that the Crown Prince had devised a plan, codenamed 'George', to break through our Front and capture Hazebrouck, so splitting the British Second Army around Ypres from the First Army in our positions forward of Béthune. Their breakthrough battle was scheduled for October but was postponed because of our own attack at Ypres. The full weight of the German attack was to have been straight through our lines at Cuinchy!

Before the year was out, the British launched the first massed tank assault in history at Cambrai. On 20th November, 496 tanks moved against the German salient across unbroken ground under a predicted barrage but without a preparatory bombardment to warn the enemy, who were taken completely by surprise. Even the redoubtable Generalfeldmarschall Rupprecht admitted that his troops were totally unprepared for this action, although he added the caveat that it was the only time in the entire war that they were caught out over a wide area. The Germans lost much ground, but as fighting continued and a counter-attack by twenty divisions was launched, we were unable to hold our gains. By 7th December, everyone was more or less back where they started; such was the nature of actions on the Western Front.

By now, my sister Lucy had joined the Women's Army Auxiliary Corps and it wouldn't be long before she too was serving in France. Our mother was soon to be regularly posting three parcels of food and clothing to her children in the war.

Talbot House [Toc H] in Poperinge. Apart from the flags and window boxes, largely unchanged in 100 years

The famous upper room at Toc H. Gilbert Talbot's battlefield cross hangs in the frame to the left of the alter.

Tubby Clayton's Lamp of Maintenance, still lit on his birthday.

Scots soldiers in Poperinge's main square.

Troops marching through the square on the way to the Ypres salient in 1917 superimposed onto a modern photo of the square.

Outside Poperinge railway station showing shell damaged buildings.
Pops was in range of many German guns and suffered accordingly.

12194 Private George Ballantyne remembered on the immense
Arras Memorial.

Chapter Fifteen

"If I should die, think this only of me:
That there's some corner of a foreign field
That is forever England. There shall be
In that richer earth a richer dust concealed;
A dust whom England bore, shaped, made aware,
Gave, once, her flowers to love, her ways to roam,
A body of England's, breathing air,
Washed by the rivers, blest by the suns of home."
The Soldier – Rupert Brooke

The blast threw me across what was left of the room. The whizz-bang must have exploded just the other side of the wall we had crouched behind. It picked me up and tossed me about like a sheaf of wheat. There was no pain, no sound, just a detached realisation that I was going to die and that this was how it would be; painless, quiet, floating. I seemed to tumble through the air in slow motion, taking in all the detail. I saw Stan below me rolling over on the floor, his steel helmet flying off and cart-wheeling ahead of him. I knew my mother would cry, and my sisters. I hoped Herbert would survive.

Then I hit the ground hard, bounced and crashed up against the far wall. The excruciating pain brought reality. No more floating, no more quiet. Gun fire rattled and cracked, shells exploded, rocks, mud, soil, and water rained down. Men were shouting, some giving orders, others calling for help. Blood poured from my leg, my head and my shoulder. I couldn't move. Still the shells exploded, the noise nearly bursting my eardrums, hurting my eyes.

Then Stan, blood streaming down his face, was kneeling over me as he tried to drag me to what shelter was left.
"Stretcher bearers, stretcher bearers!" he screamed.

Straining under his injuries, he pulled me behind another wall and frantically undid my pocket flap to get to the iodine and field dressing. Lying there, I looked down along my body to see a great red gash of flesh and the jagged piece of shrapnel that still stuck out from my leg, blood oozing from around it into the wet clay. The pain so was intense I hardly felt the iodine. The shoulder of my uniform jacket had been ripped away and more blood flowed from another wound. A shell crashed to earth nearby, more clay and stones clattered down on us. I let my head fall back onto the mud. I hadn't imagined that it would be this painful when I got hit.

"Over here," Stanley yelled at the top of his voice above the roar and clatter of gun fire. I felt the warm stream of fresh blood flow from my head, over my eye, down my cheek and into my mouth. I tasted that strange sickly tang of life; thick, sticky, slightly sweet. "Okay, chum, we've got you … morphine … you'll be all …" The detached words seemed so far off, drifting away, hollow. I had the sensation of being lifted, floating; the pain gone now. I felt nothing. I knew I was dying, slipping away. I closed my eyes, gave myself to death and sank into its waiting darkness.

The stretcher bearers took us both to the Regimental Aid Post in an old building in Cambrin, where we were seen by the Medical Officer. After some initial treatment of which I had no recollection, we were transferred to the next step in the evacuation line, the Advanced Dressing Station. At this stage of the war, the ADS teams were fully kitted out with staff and equipment to carry out emergency operations.

Some time later, I regained consciousness. The bouncing, swaying and jolting of the horse-drawn ambulance making its way along the shelled and pitted road to Béthune brought me out of my stupor. I tried to move but couldn't. I had been tucked securely into the stretcher bed that I lay on. Looking up, I gazed at the underneath of another occupied bed, and opposite, two more patients lay passively, enduring the rigours of the journey. I had obviously been operated on at the ADS, given another dose of morphine and sent on to the next stage. My leg, heavily bandaged, no longer hurt. My shoulder and head were also bandaged. With drugged sluggishness, I came to recognise the familiarity of sounds outside as we passed through a myriad of scenes along the road; distant muffled explosions, serjeants shouting orders, men calling to one another, whinnying horses, the clatter of gun carriages, an aeroplane that passed overhead. Slowly I realised what all this noise meant: I was alive, I had not died in that house after all. Through the mist of my mind, I remembered my premonition.

I tried to speak to the nurse beside me but I couldn't form the words. He patted my uninjured shoulder and said something I didn't hear as I slipped into unconsciousness again. I vaguely came round amongst the clanging of couplings and the hissing of steam in Béthune railway station where we were transferred to the waiting train for the short but much more comfortable journey to No.1 CCS at Chocques. Three hours later, I lay in the first proper bed I had been in since leaving England almost two years earlier. This bed in the fine Chateau L'Abbaye just outside the village was where my journey ended. Sleep came easily.

The doctor at the ADS had written 'AT' in large letters on my forehead in blue skin pencil to indicate to the medical staff further down the line that I had already been given an anti-tetanus injection. For the same reason, I also had a large 'M' on my wrist to show that I was already dosed up with morphine. The morphine wore off and the pain returned. They gave me more and I slept again. I lost track of time; eventually they refused any more morphine and the pain stayed. Gradually, over the days, it eased. I had been very lucky. Although my wounds would trouble me for the rest of my life, at least I would have a life. At a time before penicillin and the other antibiotics that we now take so much for granted, shrapnel wounds such as mine were highly susceptible to infection and to gangrene in particular, which reaped a terrible harvest amongst young men who today would have lived.

I was wounded on 20th March 1918 and, like the first time I saw the wolves and the Northern Lights, it remains indelibly etched in my memory. Within hours of my being hit, the Germans launched Operation Michael on the Somme in what would become the opening of their great spring offensive, known as the *Kaiserschlacht*, the Emperor's Battle. Following the Russian revolution the previous autumn and the collapse of the Eastern Front, Ludendorff was able to transfer all his troops from the east to strengthen his position in the west, but time was against him. There was industrial strife at home, food and materials shortages for his army and the threat posed by nearly two million American troops in France. It was now or never for him to win the war.

Still slow to react to the changing tactics of modern warfare, we had taken training manuals from prisoners and deserters which showed the new German *Sturmtruppen*, the storm-trooper strategy, but the committee of British major-generals in London to whom the manuals had been sent for analysis had totally failed to grasp their significance. Thus we did not adopt and train in the use of elastic defence tactics, and the well-armed but lightly equipped Sturmtruppen quickly broke through our lines on the Somme. Within two days we had retreated from all that bloodied and dearly won ground.

The German 18th Army in particular made spectacular progress, but the men were tired and hungry. The rapid progress upon the heels of the Allied retreat stretched the German forces far beyond their supply lines. Kapitän Rudolf Binding expressed it thus, "*Wie die Hölle – weiter und weiter, Tag und Nacht wir werden. Unser Gepäck ist irgendwo im Heck und wir erwarten nicht, dass es weider zu sehen.*" [We are going like hell – on and on, day and night. Our baggage is somewhere in the rear and we don't expect to see it again.] After four days on the move, the advancing troops were short of sleep, ammunition, water and food for themselves and their horses.

On their way to Amiens they arrived in Albert, where they found the shops full of food and wine. Discipline evaporated and the ravenous troops looted the town, slaking their hunger and thirst. The next morning, they were in no fit state for battle and paid the price. Although Germany was still gaining ground, she was losing men at an unsustainable rate. Gradually the attacks ran out of steam. Once again, Ludendorff's men were brought to a standstill at the River Marne.

All this was unfolding whilst I lay in my hospital bed at Chocques. The RAMC nurses and staff looked worried and gave us what news they could about the German breakthrough as they changed our dressings each day. The wound to my head healed first, and then my shoulder. Fortunately neither was as bad as might have been. My leg, though, caused greater concern. The wound was clean but I had difficulty putting my weight on it. Nevertheless, after several days I was able to get up and start to slowly walk around the garden grounds of the old chateau. In its heyday, the gardens must have been beautiful. Now, however, despite the efforts of the RAMC staff who grew vegetables and flowers there for use in the hospital, they looked tired and unkempt.

One morning, the talk was all about evacuation. The RFC observers had seen cleverly disguised evidence of a build-up of enemy forces to the south of Ypres. It was believed that, as had happened on the Somme, there might be an attack in our area. The hospital was already within range of the larger enemy guns; any advance would bring the smaller field artillery to bear. With this in mind, the hospital was cleared of the walking wounded, one of which I was now classed as, and made ready for a move to the west once more. Only those with healing and recovery complications or unable to walk were to move with the CCS. My convalescence was over before it had begun and I was returned to my unit with further treatment provided at the ADS. On 16th April, to treat the casualties coming in from the fighting in the salient towards Hazebrouck, No.1 CCS was evacuated right back to Arques on the outskirts of St Omer, more or less where it had been in November 1914.

I boarded the train back to Béthune and shortly afterwards limped into our billet. Sitting on an ammunition box in the middle of the room was Stan, smiling broadly. "Where have you been, Sapper Hill? We've been stuck here waiting for you."
It was good to see him as I had not known what had happened to him. Treated as walking wounded at the ADS, he had returned to the unit at Béthune without needing to go on to the CCS.

Barely had I settled in again when we were told to evacuate. Operation Georgette, the little brother of what would have been George in October 1917, was unleashed towards our sector from south of Ypres. Prince Rupprecht's northern forces crossed the River Lys on 9th April and the same day burned and razed Estaires, not five miles from our position at Cuinchy. Near Ypres, the Messines Ridge was re-taken, Bailleul was destroyed and the Portuguese forces were all but annihilated at Neuve Chapelle. Pushing on, the attackers reached the River Lawe, where they encountered the 51st (Highland) and 55th (West Lancashire) Divisions, which stood firm and brought the great advance to a stop. To vent its frustration, the German artillery turned on Béthune, resolved to destroy the ancient centre of the town.

We had moved from the outskirts and were now using the cellar of an abandoned house in the middle of Béthune as our base. We could hear the steady crunch of exploding shells getting closer, and then suddenly the whole building shook. Masonry tumbled down into the street and crashed through the wooden floors above us.

The officer sent one of the young sappers up the stairs to see what was going on. When he returned he reported that the whole street was burning. As at Estaires, the town was being destroyed by incendiaries. To make evacuation of the few remaining civilians even more hazardous, the streets were a death trap from the flying razor stilettos of the shrapnel shells which were coming in with the incendiaries.

So far, our front line at Cuinchy had held, but we needed to move again to a less vulnerable position. One of our serjeants and two sappers had been out to scout around. When they returned, we gathered up all our equipment and loaded it into the 15cwt truck. Because my leg was still heavily bandaged, I travelled in this whilst everyone else climbed into the larger truck. The drivers took us through all the little back streets to try to reduce the chance of being hit, although the shelling was so intense that it was more luck than anything that helped us out of the town. In every street, fires were burning out of control, sending roof tiles, timbers and stonework crashing to the ground. Our vehicles twisted and turned along the narrow streets and alleys until finally we turned onto the Beuvry road, leaving behind the blazing ruins of the little town to the enemy guns and the dusk.

A year earlier, First Army HQ had moved from Lillers to Ranchicourt and it was now vital that we kept our front-line position connected to HQ, especially as the line on both sides of us had been broken and our battalions had to fall back. The substantial width of the Canal d'Aire protected our northern flank and shaped the German advance on its north bank. However, as had happened further south, the impetus of the operation petered out, with attacking troops left exhausted and short of food and ammunition. By the end of April, the Allies had stabilised the Front and the *Kaiserschlacht* had run into the buffers. The new lines were drawn more or less where they had been at the end of 1914.

Over the next three months, the enemy made a number of offensive moves along the front, but each ended without any overall strategic advance. In response, what would come to be known as the Allied Hundred Days Offensive started with a series of attacks upon the various German salients. On 18th July, the French stemmed and then counter-attacked the Marne salient. When it ended on 5th August Germany was all but spent. Ludendorff and Kaiser Wilhelm had both come to recognise that there was no possibility of a German victory and that their great cause was lost.

Next for the Allies was the Amiens salient. Surprise was the critical element in the tank attack. As the men gathered in the hours beforehand, there was complete silence. The marshy ground and the lingering mist that covered it muffled the sound of vehicles. Drivers whispered in soothing tones to their horses and the groups of anxious men kept their thoughts to themselves. At 4.20am on 8th August the deafening barrage started as General Rawlinson's Fourth Army advanced unseen through the mist and broke the enemy lines. In just over three hours, the British, Canadian, Australian and French forces had destroyed six divisions, captured 29,144 prisoners, 338 guns, advanced nine miles and liberated 116 towns and villages. Amongst the guns captured was the great Krupp Amiens gun. It had started life as a naval gun before being adapted for land use, firing from a railway wagon. Its 45-ton barrel had rained 11 inch shells upon Amiens from over 25 miles away; its capture was a great loss to the Germans. Later, Ludendorff would describe the 8th as the Black Day of the German Army. But success for the Allies came at great cost; 21,243 casualties, of which around 5,500 were killed.

From September 1917 until March 1918, Herbert had been in the trenches at Armentières, which was not far from where I was at Béthune and Cuinchy. My parents had been officially informed that I had been wounded and had passed the news on to Herbert.

My stay in the CCS coincided with a period when Herbert's battalion was out of the line and resting. He obtained his officer's permission to come to the hospital and visit me. It was so very good to see him as I had not seen my brother since my embarkation leave almost two years earlier. He looked tired and older than his nineteen years. He had the haggard look of war weariness about him, but despite that, as always, he was cheerful.

We talked about home and how glad we would both be when the war was all over. He told me how much he was looking forward to finding a job in the new world of radio using the skills he had learned as a signaller. I asked him to write to Mother and tell her that I was only slightly wounded and that I was recovering very well and to pass the message on to Violet; I knew that they would be more likely to believe him knowing that he had seen me. All too soon, it was time for him to go. We wished each other good luck, and as he left, he turned and waved cheerily, saying, "See you at home, Roly."

From Armentières, Herbert's 15th Battalion moved to Albert, where, between April and July, they were involved in what was quaintly described as 'stationary warfare'. From 19th July until 5th August his division was resting at Hérissart before its involvement in the advance of the Hundred Days Offensive.

Wednesday 14th August was Herbert's twentieth birthday and he celebrated it by being on the receiving end of some gas shells in Heathcote's Bank trench near the Ancre river. The shelling was light and there were no injuries to anyone, but it was not how he would have chosen to spend his birthday. Three days later, the 15th Battalion was relieved by the 13th and Herbert moved with the rest to the reserve camp at location P14b. On the 19th, they were brought out of reserve and moved up to Purple Line in Englebelmer. It was time to fight for the bloodied soil of the Somme again.

The next night, at 9pm, in accordance with Battle Order 194, the 114th started to relieve the 115th and part of the 110th infantry brigades. It was 3am by the time the relief was complete and by then a thick blanket of fog hung in the valley and across much of the Somme area. The following day, patrols were sent out to reconnoitre four crossing points on the River Ancre; the enemy, though, were found to be holding the east bank in some strength.

On the 22nd, the battalion, including Herbert, moved up to the valley west of Mesnil on the opposite side of the Ancre to Thiepval. Patrolling of the river crossings continued after dusk with some success in getting men across at St Pierre-Divion without being seen. They then captured Chickweed and Common Lane trenches, the latter with twenty-five prisoners and five machine guns. Later, there was a counter-attack and the enemy retook the trenches, but undeterred, Herbert's battalion recovered them again the following afternoon after some hand-to-hand fighting. The battalion lost two men killed, sixteen wounded and one missing here.

At 1am on Saturday 24th, under the cover of mist and darkness, Herbert moved out with his battalion to wade across the Ancre river and the marshy swamps of its flood plain to start the advance up the long slog of exposed hillside towards the enemy position on Thiepval Ridge. With wet boots and squelching feet, progress on the lower slopes was covered by darkness and the fog. The defenders could not see this far into the valley, even in daylight, and thus far remained unaware of the strength of the attack.

As daylight broke just after 5am, the 15th were making good headway up the constant slope that was the side of the Thiepval Ridge. Although the ground was firm, it was hard going up and down the hummocks and dips with full battle kit and ammunition to carry, and for Herbert, he carried the huge weight of the signallers' radio set on his back. The force pressed on, higher up the hill towards the enemy. There was no other cover here. The fighting two years earlier had destroyed everything in the area, houses, trees, walls, everything. Only the shallow holes of the pock-marked battlefield offered temporary sanctuary.

In daylight, the German gunners had a clear view across the tortured ground that lay between the top of Thiepval Ridge and the lip of the Ancre valley. Like ghostly apparitions, the forward men materialised from the fog and were fully exposed to the gaze of the watching Germans. Within seconds, co-ordinated machine-gun and mortar fire swept the open fields that had once been part of Mouquet Farm. Despite the physical effort of climbing up out of the valley, the approaching soldiers, bayonets fixed, broke into as much of a run as they could towards the enemy defenders before the fire cut them all down.

The bullets ripped into my young brother's body as he neared the top of the ridge. Herbert fell where he had been hit whilst the attack moved on, leaving him behind. That day, the Welch Regiment succeeded in capturing around 1,000 prisoners, several trench mortars, a substantial quantity of supplies and many machine guns, including the one which had shot Herbert. The battalion's losses were one officer and eight other ranks killed, and twenty-seven other ranks wounded, including Herbert.

Despite heavy rain earlier in the month, the weather in mid and late August was beautiful but stiflingly hot. As the gathering heat of the day burned off the mist, the sun blazed out of clear blue skies, a haze shimmering over the hard dry ground. The stretcher bearers found Herbert unconscious but alive, just, as he lay in the gathering heat of the morning, alone and bleeding. He had lost a lot of blood and was taken back to the ADS, where they operated on the terrible wounds caused by the machine-gun bullets. After this initial surgery, he was evacuated by ambulance and train to No.38 CCS at Fienvillers between Abbeville and Doullens. At the CCS, Herbert was given a blood transfusion, which at the time was a very new medical procedure and was mainly a result of the Americans coming into the war and the work of Oswald Robertson.

Although a small and rather sleepy French village now, during the war, Fienvillers was an important base to us, at various times housing No.34 and No.38 CCS, as well as an RFC/RAF aerodrome, which was home to many squadrons, No.2 Aircraft Depot, the repair section known as No.2 Aeroplane Supply Depot, a Scout squadron and, from 1916 until the spring of 1918, the RFC HQ.

Herbert was nursed at the CCS for three days with the best skills that they had, but despite everything that was done for him there, he died on 28th August, two weeks after his birthday. He is buried in Fienvillers British Military Cemetery.

The La Bassée Front has often been referred to as the Forgotten Front because after the abortive attack against the German 6th Bavarian Reserve Division on 19th–20th July 1916, it was not the scene of any major offensives, even though there was a constant battle between the two sides over the very narrow stretch of No Man's Land, not least the battle that took place beneath the ground with the laying of mines under or close to each other's trenches.

Now that the wider front had been broken in several places, the First Army at last moved forward, although not very rapidly, pushing across that decimated sector, past the Brickworks, through Douvrin and on to a succession of short objectives towards the east. We had no idea that we were on the final push to victory, thinking instead that at the German border the enemy would dig in and the war would return to trench stalemate. The weather was once again very wet and we advanced through pouring rain and heavy mud. The difference this time, though, was that the

Germans were trying to retreat through that same rain and mud rather than defend a static position. The result was that their heavy guns and equipment got bogged down and trapped as ours had so often done in the past, most famously the year before at Passchendaele, forcing them to abandon their artillery. It was a double loss; we had captured it and they were denied its further use.

Over these weeks, there was little rest for the REs as we advanced with the troops, laying lines to ensure that they were always in telephone contact with the various HQs. We had very little sleep, and whilst the enemy may have been retreating at an increasing rate, he did not do so quietly or willingly. Shells and mortars continued to pose a permanent threat to us whilst working in the open to lay the wires.

I had learned to live and work with the daily shelling and ever-present threat of snipers that we experienced at Cuinchy and Béthune, but being wounded had affected me badly. The whining sound of shells passing overhead, whether they were ours or theirs, unsettled me, and I had become very edgy and jumpy. I found myself flinching every time one exploded anywhere nearby, which was not good as we were often subjected to spells of intense mortar fire from troops covering a withdrawal as our own forces advanced. The wound to my leg had still not completely healed and caused me a lot of pain. Sleeping for more than a few minutes at a time had become increasingly difficult to achieve even though I was utterly exhausted.

One evening towards the end of September we had returned to the relative warmth and comfort of the barn which was our temporary billet when the serjeant came in and handed out the mail. There was still nothing for me. I had not had any news from home since the advance started. After handing round all the mail, he told me that the officer wanted to see me in his room in the farm house at once.   Thinking that this sounded like another special and unpleasant job coming my way in the rain that was once more pouring down, I limped across the yard to the house where the officer's servant [his batman] was waiting to show me upstairs.

Our officer, by now promoted to captain, had always been good with his men and he was again that night. When he told me to sit down I knew that this was not about work. He handed me a letter from my mother.
"Is that from home, Hill?"
"Yes sir, it's from my mother."
"Well, I don't know what she has written, but before you read it, I'm afraid I have some bad news for you. I'm sorry to tell you that your brother has been killed."
His words hit me like a hammer. I felt my stomach tighten. Not Herbert; it couldn't be.
"Could there be a mistake, sir?"
"I'm afraid not. I have a Signals officer friend in the Welch. I had the news from him yesterday. Your brother was wounded attacking the Thiepval Ridge at the end of last month and died in hospital."

He knew that my leg still had to be dressed by the medics every day and that I had not been able to convalesce properly. He told me that I was overdue leave. It was more than a year since my few days at Poperinge and I had not been home since May 1916. He had arranged for me to have two weeks' leave so that I could get home and spend some time with my parents. My leave was effective immediately, 29th September. I was to get something to eat, pack and be at the station before dawn.

Back in the barn, I poured a mug of tea from the pot, tipped my saved tot of rum into it and sat down to read my mother's letter. As I read her words I shared her pain. I had lost several friends in that bloody war, but the death of my own and only brother cut me deeper than I could have imagined. I thought back to his parting words as I lay in my hospital bed at Chocques six months earlier. And still the rain drummed on the pantile roof.

We were close to the railway, and by dawn, I was on a train going through to the coast at Calais. I queued for delousing, collected a clean uniform and caught the evening sailing. I was in Dover before dark and London before midnight. I bought a sandwich and a cup of tea from the Paddington Station Salvation Army stand, which never closed even on a Sunday, whilst I waited for the first train to Shrewsbury. It was 10.09 when, in brighter weather than I had left France, I stepped out of the carriage onto the platform at Cressage. Five minutes later, I walked through the door of Jasmine Cottage. I was home.

My mother was sitting in her chair by the fire holding Herbert's old cap. She looked up as I walked in. Never an emotional woman, her raw red eyes gave her away. I knelt by her chair and held her hand. I felt my sister Nellie's arm around my shoulder.

Those of us at home went to church the following Sunday and, seeing us there, the vicar, the Reverend John Lee, made a special mention of Herbert's life, his sacrifice for freedom, and a prayer for us in our grief. After the service, many of the congregation came and spoke to me about the war, some wanting to know about the two inch vertical stripe of gold Russia braid which was sewn onto my left sleeve; it was my wound stripe.

The sadness which accompanied my leave was compounded when I learned that Lady Harnage was very ill and not expected to live much longer. She had been such an important figure in the life of Cressage for more than thirty years and she would be greatly missed by many people, not least all the young men who she had helped to get a foot on the ladder of life and make something of themselves. In retrospect, though, the world was never the same again after the war and I do not think that she would have liked the momentous changes which were to come.

Violet had gone to work for Lady Harnage at the age of thirteen, when she left school in 1909. She had replaced one of the maids her Ladyship had brought with her to Littlecote from the Hall, and who had retired. As a young teenager in service Violet received one afternoon off each month. On that day she would catch the train from Cressage to Buildwas, change platforms from Low to High Level and then on to Much Wenlock, where her parents lived above the bank. In the evening, her father would accompany her for some of the 3½ mile walk back to Littlecote. By the time the war started, Vi was almost eighteen and had more free time, although she still visited her parents every month. Elizabeth Harnage died on 9th October. The house was sold and Violet went back to live with her parents in Wenlock.

My exchange of letters with Vi had at first been friendly and platonic; two people, familiar with each other, their home surroundings and background, exchanging news about familiar subjects. However, these letters had become much more personal and intimate during the last twelve months. I had found that I could confide in Vi in a way that I could not have done with my mother. I could share so much more with her about the war, what I was doing, my feelings, my fears and anxieties, our conditions and dangers. Even allowing for the censor, which anyway became increasingly relaxed, I was able to write more freely to Vi than to my parents. It was out of that intimacy that a different relationship grew, one in which it was clear we each held the other in great and increasing affection.

She would turn twenty-two ten days after I was due back in France and it would be another year at least before I was home again. I couldn't expect her to keep waiting if I didn't give her some commitment and so we let people know that we were stepping out together. This brought a little touch of joy in an otherwise solemn leave, although it would have been nice for Lady Harnage to have known since it was she who had introduced us.

By nightfall on 13th October, I was back in France with my unit. Four days later, the final advance towards Germany began and the alliance of the Central Powers quickly fell apart. On 29th, the sailors of the Kaiserliche Marine in Kiel mutinied, occupied the city and revolution spread. The next day, Turkey signed an Armistice. Austria-Hungary followed on 3rd November, and on Saturday 9th the Kaiser abdicated. So do the mighty stumble and fall.

For the British, the war had started at Mons. Just over four years later, after millions of deaths and devastating injuries, with large swathes of France and Belgium laid to waste, it ended at Mons. At 5am on Monday morning, Germany signed the Armistice to take effect at the 11th hour of the 11th day of the 11th month. In many areas, particularly the Meuse-Argonne Offensive, the fighting continued right to the end. The last Allied soldier to die before the ceasefire was American, Henry Nicholas Gunther, at 10.59am. His death was undoubtedly his own fault as the machine gunner who shot him did so in self-defence for, aware that the end was only a minute away, he had tried to warn Gunther, whose parents were German though naturalised Americans, not to charge the gun position. Ignoring the warning brought his inevitable death.

Thus the last Allied soldier to fall to deliberate hostile action was Canadian, George Lawrence Price from Falmouth, Nova Scotia, who was shot in the chest by a sniper at 10.58am whilst searching for a machine gunner that had been harassing his patrol. The name of the last German soldier to die in the conflict has eluded me.

These, however, are the officially recorded names. When the end came, there was no great rejoicing, no throwing up of hats, no cheering. In places, the artillery seemed to be using every last shell whilst they could, some beyond the hour, with the inevitable consequences; those deaths are recorded after the Armistice, albeit in the war area. Although there was not a universal ceasefire or a sudden falling silent of the guns at 11 o'clock on the dot, it did generally stop at the appointed time. The overwhelming emotion felt by the thousands of men and women who had been caught up in this futile and wholly avoidable conflict for so long was one of exhausted relief; a conflict which had been brought about by just a handful of vengeful and intransigent men.

As the hour came and then passed, with the growing calm, I came to realise that I had survived. How I wished Herbert could have seen this day too. That night, we made a bonfire and sat around it drinking tea heavily laced with rum to fight off the growing cold. From habit we made sure that the fire could not be seen from the other side. It would be many months before I could start to no longer think about the possibility of snipers or shells wherever I went. We were all the same.

After the signing of the Armistice, the British, French and Americans each established occupation zones on the east bank of the Rhine. Although the fighting had ceased, the Germans had not surrendered; the Armistice was a ceasefire, hence the occupation force. The war did not formally end until the signing of the Treaty of Versailles on 28th June 1919.

In the immediate aftermath of the fighting, the Air Line Coy remained in France and was engaged in clearing up and recovering as much of our telephone equipment and associated materials as possible before we finally all went home. Retrieving what we could meant working and digging in old trenches and across fiercely fought-over ground. The rats still abounded although numbers noticeably dwindled as their various food sources disappeared.

It became inevitable that we unearthed the remains of bodies or parts of bodies that had not been found and collected at the time of their deaths. Those more recently killed in the old trenches had generally already been recovered; it was those that had become lost by time and shellfire that we tended to find. We often knew before we found them. The air, which was already unpleasant to breathe, filled with that familiar stench I had first smelled at Cuinchy in 1916.

Sometimes they were ours, sometimes theirs, but all of them men who had once lived and breathed as we still did; all loved by someone. Despite the emotional hardening that comes with war, it was still a harrowing experience to come across the remains of these men.

Immediately following the end of the war, the army created exhumation units whose job it was to find, recover and try to identify fallen soldiers for burial in newly created war cemeteries. Between the Armistice and September 1921, the army reburied 204,695 bodies. In February 1921, the responsibility for maintaining these cemeteries passed to the Imperial War Graves Commission, now called the Commonwealth War Graves Commission. Although formal searches ended in 1921, over the next three years, a further 38,000 bodies were discovered and continue to be so, even now, a hundred years later.

Whenever we found someone we would notify the exhumation section and they would come for the body. However, it was never that quick or simple and, because we were sappers, we were often ordered to carry on and dig out the man's remains, preferably along with his dog tag, and make a note of where he was found. Finding the dog tag was a very important part of recovering a body but it required a strong stomach. Occasionally the body was little more than a skeleton, though usually it would be in an advanced state of decomposition. But whatever the condition, and however much or little we could find, it would be placed on a makeshift stretcher and covered over, awaiting collection and a proper dignified burial.

It wasn't only the bodies of soldiers that we found. In some areas the most usual body found was that of an animal. I had seen so many dead and dying animals during the fighting and now I had to see them again. Millions of animals were used by the belligerents during the war and huge numbers of them perished. In addition to the fine cavalry steeds, working horses were found in most areas of the army. Clydesdales were the mainstay of the artillery, hauling the heavy guns and ammunition trailers around the battlefield. Dogs and pigeons were also heavily used. Pigeons were important message carriers, especially over long distances. Dogs were also used as messengers as their speed and agility made them much more likely to succeed than a man. The RAMC enlisted them as first aid carriers and the RE used them for laying telephone wires from a drum strapped on their backs.

The losses amongst these animals were immense. Britain lost some 484,000 horses, and by 1917, the life of a horse had become strategically more valuable than that of a man. However, most horses did not die from wounds but as a result of disease, exhaustion or the same lethal mud that sucked down so many soldiers. There are, though, many stories of the remarkable courage shown by animals during the war, creatures who served their masters unflinchingly and without any understanding of why they were there.

Throughout the war, the women of France and Belgium who lived close to wherever there were troops had scratched a living selling a wide variety of wares popular with the troops. A great favourite for those with a wife or girlfriend at home were the lovely sweetheart cards, especially at Christmas time. Early in the war, when materials were more freely available, these had often been embroidered with silk thread and many were exquisitely made. Now that the fighting was over, I missed Vi more than ever and was impatient to be demobbed so that our lives together could begin. Just before Christmas 1918 I managed to buy one of these sweetheart cards to send to her. After the horrors of the last two and a half years, it was good to feel and celebrate this sort of emotion again.

Our billets remained in broken-down buildings and cellars, and as the cold, wet winter weather set in, my leg wound troubled me greatly and I was not passed medically fit to go into Germany as part of the occupation force. At the end of January 1919 I was given ten days' medical leave in France to have some further treatment on my leg. I was sent to No.35 General Hospital at Calais, one of the many that still remained in France. I was admitted for treatment but was able to come and go as I pleased once my daily dressings had been done, which, despite the weather, made a very pleasant change and was a reminder both of normality and of what we had fought for. Nevertheless, it was with some melancholy that I looked across the Channel towards England, knowing that I could not yet go home.

When I returned to my unit it was to light duties only. The doctors were concerned that if I continued digging in the wet, mud and slime of the old battlefields, my leg would become infected and if so, I would probably lose it. Then, at the beginning of May, my officer told me that I had fourteen days' leave in England.
"Make sure you take all your kit with you, Hill. You'll be pleased to know that you won't be coming back." He smiled, then added, "Thank you for everything you've done. I'm glad you survived it all."
He stood up and reached out his hand to me. I shook it and thanked him. He had been a good officer to us all and had looked after us. I was glad he had survived too.

In the early light of 5th May, I loaded my heavy kitbag into the back of the truck that was going to take me to Abbeville and climbed in the open-fronted cab next to the driver. At Abbeville I would catch the train to the coast and from there cross to England. It was the reverse of the journey I had made almost exactly three years earlier.

We bumped along making steady progress and at Doullens swung onto the road for Abbeville. As we did so, I caught sight of a small hand-painted sign to Fienvillers, five miles along the same road. Knowing that Fienvillers had been a major base and aerodrome in the war, I asked the driver if he had been there before and if he knew where the CCS was. He did, but said that both Nos.34 and 38 CCS had closed the previous September. I explained that Herbert had died in the hospital, was buried there and that I would like to visit him since we were passing.

The graves are in a small secluded corner of a field a short way down a narrow country lane. The cemetery was created by the CCS staff and now contains 124 graves. It is a lovely quiet and peaceful place for Herbert to rest. I found his grave in the third row back from the road, marked by the simple wooden cross made by a local French carpenter and placed there by the hospital staff when he was buried. I knelt before my brother's grave and cried. Why did it have to be Herbert? Why so close to the end? My little brother, my only brother; gone. It was as if all the emotions that I had had to keep so tightly locked away for so long just boiled up and flowed out of me.

Presently, I felt a hand on my shoulder; it was one of the IWGC staff working on site. He asked me if I should like to see Herbert's headstone of Stancliffe sandstone that would soon be put in place, after which the wooden cross would, in accordance with IWGC practice, be sent home to Cressage. The stone bore the emblem of the Welch Regiment, Herbert's number, rank and name, the date of his death, a cross and the words my mother had chosen to be added, "*Father, in Thy gracious keeping, leave we now our dear one sleeping.*"

The peacefully rural setting of Fienvillers Military Cemetery

My brother's grave in Fienvillers Military Cemetery

Iwan [front left sitting on the grass] convalescing with other casualties of the 6th Canadian Machine Gun Company at Seaford in 1917

Seven stretcher bearers struggling to carry a wounded comrade through the mud of Passchendaele

Near to the site of No.1 CCS as it is today. The old Chateau L'Abbaye which housed part of the CCS, no longer exists.

Chapter Sixteen

"Here during a period which is too long while it lasts and too short when it is over, we may placidly reflect on the busy world that lies behind and the tumult that is before us."
London to Ladysmith via Pretoria – Winston S Churchill [1900]

Tuesday 6th May found me once more at Cressage station. My father was there to meet me this time and we slowly walked through the village and along Wood Lane to Jasmine Cottage. It was good to be home. The weather was beautiful. The sun shone all day from a cloudless sky as it had done for the last few days. It was in fact to be the start of a prolonged drought that lasted well into June without a drop of rain. The cottage looked as it had always done, unchanged by the tumult in the world. It was a point of reference, a symbol of certainty, and yet I already knew that nothing would really be the same as it was before the war.

The next day I took the train to Much Wenlock to see Vi and we spent a wonderful few hours together at last free from the worry of my return to war. My leave passed all too quickly again, at the end of which I travelled down to Brompton Barracks at Chatham, where I spent the rest of my service. I was demobbed on 18th August 1919, two days after my twenty-seventh birthday. I was due various sums of money from the army, which came to me over the next fortnight and totalled £22-3s-3d. The money included twenty-eight days' holiday pay at my daily rate of 5/6d. However, the Government charged me £1 for keeping my trusty greatcoat that had seen me through two and a half years in the trenches. My contribution to the Kaiser's defeat was, it appeared, not even worth £1!

Once I was out of the wet and the mud of the trenches and had started to sleep in a bed again, my leg healed quickly, and by the time of my demob, I was once again passed as medically fit, 'A' class. This was very important to me in my hope of returning to work for the Post Office as a lineman. Much later in life, though, the shrapnel which remained embedded in my leg would come back to trouble and pain me.

As the emotional and physical pressures had been relieved I began to sleep for longer spells at a time and gradually overcame the lingering effects of the prolonged exhaustion I, like all the others, had been exposed to. It was around this time that I started to suffer the nightmares which would stay with me and would intermittently recur. Scenes that I had witnessed, the shells that had come so close, the bodies I had seen, tortured faces rising up from the mud; memories that would never fade.

By the time I returned to civilian life, Herbert's battlefield cross had been sent home to my parents. Always close to the church as a family, they had taken it to John Lee and, at the following Sunday service, he had blessed the cross and given thanks for Herbert's all-too-short life. Thereafter, that cross hung in the entrance porch to the church, a reminder to all of the human cost of war.

I had kept in touch with the various friends who had survived the fighting. Iwan had recovered from his 1917 wounds, but a more enlightened Canadian regime had returned him home to the farm whilst he was still in one piece rather than send him back to the fighting. Bob Fernihough had not been quite so lucky. Having been in at the beginning, he had remained a stretcher bearer with his RAMC unit to the bitter end. When it was all over, unsurprisingly, Bob succumbed to shell shock. A gentle man of quiet disposition, he had endured the shells for four years. In the end, it was just too much. When peace came and the pressure to preserve life was lifted from his shoulders, he collapsed; a wreck of a man. Even after he recovered, Bob was never the same again.

His hands always shook; he had difficulty holding his thoughts and even more difficulty articulating them. He never married and was looked after by his younger sister. He was fortunate that the family still had the grocer's business in Bolton for he was, as with so many like him, abandoned by the army and the country he had served so valiantly.

With the approach of the end of army life in sight, I had registered my wish to rejoin the GPO as an experienced Permanent Lineman. Having inspected my demobilisation papers, my application was accepted by the GPO and it was with great relief that on 19th August 1919, my first day back in Civvy Street, I received a letter from the Hanley office, Stoke-on-Trent, informing me that I should report there for duty on Monday 15th September. I would need some transport to get to and from work and so used some of my savings to buy a motor cycle.

In the meantime, I helped out on the farm and slowly became reacclimatised to civilian life. Having this month before starting at Hanley suited me very well as I was able to see Vi most days. It wasn't long before we decided to marry and set the date for the following June. My priority now was to find somewhere for us to live and I was able to rent rooms at 22, Sheinton Street in Wenlock.

Unlike the stunning May weather of the year before, the first half of May 1920 was cool and wet, although things did brighten up after the 20th. As June arrived, although it remained warm, it was a muggy heat and we had several very violent thunderstorms, some throwing down hailstones more than half an inch across. Working outside on the farm in those conditions was impossible and we had to find cover somewhere.

There were times when the sky became so dark it seemed as if the apocalypse was drawing nigh. Lightning forked out of the sky at a ferocious rate and rain came down in a wall of water that washed soil and crops from the fields, dug channels in the roadways and flooded the slightest dip in the ground in moments. But it was the thunder that I had come to hate. Every crack, crash and rumble put me back on the Western Front. I was not the only one who had been through that hell who reacted like that; we were all the same, unconsciously cowering under a hedge or in a building as a reflex action to the sound of nature's barrage. Sometimes I found myself huddled tightly in a corner waiting for the shell to explode and send me hurtling across the room. The thunder that month was so intense it just felt like being in France again.

Finally, our wedding day arrived. Violet and I were married at the 12th-century Holy Trinity Parish Church in Wenlock on Wednesday 30th June. After all the bad weather that year, we were lucky enough to have a dry, if not particularly warm or sunny day for our wedding. This was all the more important since Violet walked to church from her home. Cars were still a rarity in 1920, for the most part, owned only by the wealthy, although not all, by any means. Thus most brides still either walked to their wedding or rode by carriage. The service was conducted by Violet's great friend, Prebendary EB Bartleet, who had confirmed her nine years earlier on 2nd April 1911 and who had helped and encouraged her when I was in France.

After we were married, Vi gave up work to look after the house. Although I still had some of my army back pay and my savings from Canada to help us out, we had to be careful what we spent. I had by now transferred from Hanley to Shrewsbury which sometimes meant working away from home in North Wales. My weekly rate of pay was £1-12s-6d [£1.62½p].

In April 1921, I received my British War Medal, and then in August the Victory Medal followed. I was immensely proud of them and yet they didn't seem much to represent the enormity of it all, the horror, and the sacrifice that we had made in that terrible war and none more so than Herbert. All I could do now was to hope that it would never be repeated and that it really had been a war to end all wars – but I had my doubts.

I knew that by working for the GPO we would never be well-off, but I also knew that we would not starve. We were able to pay our way and have enough left over for me to buy another motor cycle. The GPO provided me with a secure job, a steady income and a pension later in life. In the years to come, as the world economy came to a virtual standstill in the 1930s and men were laid off in their millions, these would be important considerations.

Our first child was Mary, then in October 1922 Rowland, who was baptised on 3rd December the following year, was born. Now that we had two children, we needed some better transport with more seats than the pillion, but a car was out of the question. I had seen that year's model four-stroke Sunbeam motor cycle and sidecar in the shop window with a price tag of £130. In the days before credit it took me a year to save for it, but at last I bought the outfit which gave us many happy days out as a family. At first, Vi would ride on the pillion and the children would sit in the sidecar. Later, as Rowland grew a little older, he and his mother changed places.

That motor cycle travelled many miles and never let me down. I kept it for thirty-four years before selling it in 1957 to Bill Doran, the motor cycle shop owner in Wellington. I was very pleased when Bill bought it from me because I knew that it would be well ridden and well cared for. In fact, Bill often rode it in the London to Brighton and other vintage motor cycle rallies.

Wenlock is famous for being the birthplace of the modern Olympics in 1850, thanks to Dr William Penny Brookes. However, the annual events became more intermittent after Dr Brookes' death in 1895, and following the war, there was little interest for some years. At this time, Wenlock was an independent borough covering 71 square miles and included Ironbridge. With its own administration, court, fire service and market, the Borough of Wenlock was the largest in England outside London.

In the 1920s, life in Wenlock was hard, basic and generally quiet so long as you obeyed the law. Those who didn't would come before the magistrates in the ancient court room and receive sentence. The town had become very run down and dowdy in the 18th century, with contemporary accounts describing it variously as '*a very paltry, dirty town*' and '*...two ill-built streets, and standing low, is so dirty, that strangers, by way of derision, call it Muck Wenlock.*' As a result of this, its industry and rather isolated location, it lacked much 19th-century development. Ironically, by 1900 it was already being admired for its quaint and historical character of medieval timber-framed buildings.

It was all a very far cry from the life of the Bright Young Things and London's socialite circles. They were the outrageously flamboyant, promiscuous, decadent, drug-taking, hard-drinking, smoking, jazz-loving, glamorous and irresponsible young women with their entourage of young men who created the image of the Roaring Twenties. Every young generation thinks that it is the first to discover sex, drugs and rock 'n' roll, but of course it isn't. The Bright Young Things, their followers and imitators were, though, the first to create a lifestyle that is still reflected in all that is charmless, graceless and useless in today's 'celebrity' culture.

The flapper girls of the 1920s, a look created by Coco Chanel, who in 1919 had given the world its most famous perfume, were the good-time girls of their generation. They were joined by similarly minded young men, created their own argot and partied endlessly, smoked hash, snorted cocaine and injected heroine. This was the generation who had just missed the war, having been born in 1900 or later. In a world at peace through the exhaustion that had followed the fighting, *carpe diem* was their motto. Not old enough to fight, but old enough to know about the human cost of that war, they lived each day as their last. The original 'It' Girl, Elizabeth Ponsonby, partied and drank herself to death before she reached forty, and actress Brenda Dean Paul was either in prison or rehab. These society creatures often exhibited obscene extravagance of wealth when many in the country were struggling with the reality of building, or indeed rebuilding, lives, relationships, careers and families. There was no sympathy whenever any of them slipped and fell from grace.

Although some were genuinely rich, for most it was a veneer. The large country estates were being broken up and sold. Crippling death duties were heaped upon families whose heirs lay beneath French and Belgian soil next to the sons of their staff. A paucity of money, servants and eligible heirs, coupled with social change, in particular women becoming more independent, all conspired to ensure that the peacetime clock was not going to be reset to the summer of 1910. The war had stripped away many of the royal households of Europe, and those who had stood and fought for Britain across the battlefields of the world, rich and poor alike, wanted and needed to see a change.

On Tuesday 4th May 1926 the TUC-organised General Strike began. Its roots lay in the coal industry's decline; the loss of overseas markets following the war, the fall in demand at home and the huge reduction in miners' wages. It would take many more disputes, strikes and lock-outs, the collapse of a government and another seventy years before the industry would finally be laid to rest. In the long term, the miners would lose their livelihoods, the employers would lose their businesses and the country would lose its resource. Coal created over 300 million years ago in the warm tropical Carboniferous swamps of the land that would become Britain would stay undisturbed in the ground. The wealth of its fossil record and the pollution of its carbon store both locked away forever.

Like the lifestyle of the Bright Young Things, the General Strike passed Wenlock by. It was called off after six days and people returned to work; in time, the striking miners did too, although some of the organisers were never employed again.

Good times never last forever and the Roaring Twenties were no exception. If the 1926 General Strike dimmed the party atmosphere of the decade then the 1929 Wall Street Crash turned the lights out. In late October that year, the Dow Jones lost 25% of its value in two days and plunged America into an economic depression. For many socialites here the money had run out too. The paparazzi press were tiring of these petulant, irresponsible wastrels, and for those who were still able to afford membership of the 'club', the November 1931 Red and White Ball was the straw that broke the camel's back. Everything was red and white, including the food. When unemployment was already relentlessly high, when recession had turned to depression, the extravagance of it all was too much. Roundly denounced, the flame of the Bright Young Things was extinguished as easily as it had been lit.

Nevertheless, it was not all a sad waste and, then like now, they were not all without talent; indeed some had considerable and genuine ability. Out of the mess emerged some remarkable people; William Walton, John Betjeman and Cecil Beaton, each of whom were later knighted, Noel Coward, Evelyn Waugh, two of the famous Mitford sisters, Diana and Nancy [all the sisters were talented, but not all were recognised BYTs], Edith Sitwell, who was later made a Dame, and her two younger brothers, Osbert and Sacheverell, Siegfried Sassoon MC, the accomplished war poet who could and should also have been awarded the VC and DSO for his actions on the Western Front, along with many others.

Perhaps the most enduring cultural influence that emerged in the 1920s and developed further through the 1930s was jazz, which then developed into the great dance music of the 1940s. Its origins lay with the African Americans of the southern United States and New Orleans in particular. At the turn of the century, when improvisations of popular songs in the natural rhythm of traditional African music, ragtime and blues were all played without sheet music in the street and at social functions, the sound became known as 'jass' or 'jazz'. It was quickly adopted by white musicians and did much to help break down the segregated world that existed then.

In France, the American troops had had portable gramophones and I had quickly learned to like jazz. I heard quite a lot of it after the war when we were clearing up and often spent evenings with the Americans in the estaminets.

The popularity of the gramophone, various radio programmes and, perversely, alcohol prohibition, all helped to spread jazz and the dances that accompanied it throughout America and, inevitably, across the Atlantic to Britain. The introduction of alcohol prohibition in the States in 1920 brought the dance halls, clubs and speakeasies. In all these places, jazz was the music, and the Black Bottom, Charleston, Fox Trot and Shimmy were the dances that excited the customers. The great depression of the thirties slowed everything down across the world as money became scarce for too many people. In America, unemployment in the southern states forced thousands to migrate to the northern cities of Detroit and Chicago in search of work, taking their jazz music with them.

Long before Scottish inventor John Logie Baird gave television to the world, dancing was the most popular leisure activity in all walks of life. By 1923, jazz had become popular in Britain and was even broadcast by the BBC. To meet the growing demand of an increasing radio audience, the BBC broadcast regular live performances from different venues. The British Broadcasting Company, as it was then, first broadcast on 14th November 1922. The following year, the company moved to premises at Savoy Hill, off the Strand. This would be an inspirational choice, for nearby was the Savoy Hotel, from where the BBC would broadcast live the music of the resident and guest dance bands for the next thirty years.

Not quite as chic but just as popular was the Wenlock brass band and working men's club at the Corn Exchange. Sometimes a neighbour would watch Mary and Rowland so that Violet and I could go there in the evening to a dance. Even in Wenlock, jazz was becoming popular, and I had some of the 78rpm shellac records, which were now easily available, of British and American bands and combos. As the 1930s progressed, the larger dance bands became very popular, and then by the 1940s, people such as Artie Shaw, Carroll Gibbons, Roy Fox, Ambrose, Tommy Dorsey, Billy Cotton, Harry Roy, Benny Goodman, Glenn Miller and singers like Helen Forrest, Anne Shelton, Vera Lynn and Al Bowlly were all household names, thanks to the expansion of radio broadcasts and shops selling the records.

The popularity of the cinema continued to grow in the thirties as people tried to escape the harsh reality and hardship of daily life for a few hours. The influence of Hollywood dance sequences especially by Fred Astaire and Ginger Rogers such as in "Flying Down to Rio" in 1933, "Top Hat" in 1935 and "Swing Time" the following year, all helped to keep dancing popular. The jitterbug, the lindy hop and the jive became favourites, and soon the young and the not so young were once more swinging along to the music and the bands.

Wenlock's Corn Exchange was the venue for a variety of entertainments in these years and films were regularly shown there. Mary and Rowland had been attending the National School in Downs Lane on the northern boundary of the church grounds close to the old Abbey, and as they grew a little older, we were able to leave them at home alone whilst we went to see whatever was showing or to a dance. These were the days when people did not think about locking their doors, when everyone knew their neighbours and incidents of crime were generally very low. Babysitting was not a word we knew. Children did what they were told and people looked out for each other.

My work with the GPO carried on apace as telephones continued to gain in popularity and increasingly came to be seen as a necessity for many, especially doctors and vets. The job, though, was not without its lighter moments. Harley Bank carries the main A458 road down the steep scarp slope of Wenlock Edge to the pretty village of Harley, which nestles close to the bottom of the dale. From Harley, the ancient roadway invites the traveller to attack the slope head on; but this is a deceptive climb. Halfway up, all momentum gone, our traveller must swing to his left through ninety degrees and then, climbing parallel to the Edge as the road clings to the limestone rock, he must labour up the long steep incline to the top without respite. On one side, the tree-covered limestone slope reaches high above, whilst on the other, it drops sharply away into the dale far below.

In 1925, a heavily laden lorry belonging to Joseph Fish of Bristol had made its way through Wenlock and, at the top of Harley Bank, the driver, chatting to his mate beside him, had slowed the lorry and brought it down through the gearbox before starting down the almost 1:10 gradient. To slow the lorry further as it began the descent, the driver pressed down on the brake pedal. With horror, he felt his foot go all the way to the floor; his brakes had failed. By now the wagon was on its way down the steep incline, its weight pushing it ever faster, its engine screaming. The driver knew they were running away out of control.

Beside him, his companion gripped the seat for all he was worth and prayed, for he could see the right-angled bend in the road and the cottage that stood at its apex looming ahead. Recognising the hopelessness of their situation, the driver took the only choice left to him. He turned the steering wheel and edged his vehicle into the rising side of the hill, bumping along the rocks, gradually slowing the heavy vehicle and bringing it to a thankful stop. Unfortunately, just as the wagon stopped, it collided with a telegraph pole which was carrying forty-four lines from Shrewsbury and in an instant managed to take out all of Wenlock's telephones.

The main road had to be closed to traffic, not that there was a great deal in those days. A photographer turned up to find that the lorry was still stuck in the hillside and the pole was leaning over the road at 45°, with me twenty feet up it trying to sort out the mess of wires. It made a dramatic picture and Violet obtained and kept a copy, which she entitled, 'Roly up the pole'!

By the time that Mary and Rowland were at the national school, the buildings had fallen into a rather sad state of repair. The school had been built in 1847, and had for most of that time been considered the best national school by the government inspectors, the OFSTED of the day, but despite being extended and improved several times, sixty years of use by generations of children had taken its toll.

In 1928, I was promoted and we moved to Wellington where I was to be based. I was sorry to leave Wenlock, but it was a good promotion at a time when Mary and Rowland were growing up. We moved to Montgomery Road and the children went to the national school, first in Wrekin Road and then later to Constitution Hill. For more than fifty years, Wellington had been blessed with a greater number of quality, publicly funded schools than any other town in the county, and so after a good grounding, when Rowland left school at fourteen he moved on to the technical college to receive further training in mechanics.

His future was shaped by two very similar incidents, twenty-four years apart. When Britain sent the BEF across to France in 1914, although vets, doctors and nurses were included, no dentist sailed with it, which was a surprising omission since during the Boer War more than 2,000 British troops had to be sent back to Britain for dental treatment. It wasn't only men from poorer families who suffered from dental decay but officers too, even at the very highest level. In November 1914, General Haig, Commander of the First Army, was labouring under the pain of chronic toothache. Unable to find a dentist anywhere in the British Army in France, his ADC made enquiries in Paris. Auguste Charles Valadier was sent to treat the Commander-in-Chief's errant tooth.

There is nothing quite like personal experience to focus the mind, and Haig was now only too acutely aware of the miseries which poor dental care imposed upon his troops. He called for dentists to be sent to France immediately. By the end of the month, twelve had been commissioned as lieutenants and had arrived in the RAMC. The number continued to rapidly increase until the end of the war. Then, in 1921, the Army Dental Corps was formed. The 'Royal' prefix would come in 1946.

Valadier's offer of his services to the French government at the beginning of the war had been rejected because he was not a naturalised Frenchmen. He now repeated that offer to the British and was eagerly accepted. In 1915, he was joined by New Zealander Harold Gillies, and between them, they pioneered the role of dental work in the treatment of maxillo-facial trauma. Later, they were both knighted for their pioneering work in this field.

Twenty-five years after Gillies had joined Valadier in France, he was again at the forefront of treating trauma when, with his cousin Archibald McIndoe, he pioneered facial reconstruction and plastic surgery techniques on the burns suffered by RAF pilots during the

Battle of Britain. Although everyone and anyone could be treated at East Grinstead, airmen were particularly prone to being burned in aeroplane crashes.

In early 1938, Rowland, like General Haig, suffered a toothache which needed some treatment. He went to John Dickin, the dentist at Queen Street Chambers, and it was this visit which ignited his interest in dentistry. It was the mechanical engineering side which he liked; the processes and making of false teeth, plates and so on. He talked to his schoolmaster, Mr C Lowe at the technical college, and an apprenticeship with Dickin was arranged. The 18th April 1938 was Easter Monday Bank Holiday and so Rowland's five-year apprenticeship began the next day with his formal indenture dated the 19th, which I also had to sign giving my approval as the father of a minor.

At fifteen, my son entered the world of work. His hours were 9am to 6pm, Monday to Friday and 9am to 1pm on Saturday. He had two weeks' holiday plus statutory holidays. There was no sick pay, so no work, no money. For his working week, he was to be paid five shillings in the first year, ten shillings in the second and fifteen shillings in the third. To reflect his acquired skills and usefulness to the practice, this would rise to £1-7s-6d in year four and £1-15s-0d in his final year.

The 1930s brought depression, progress, political unrest and finally war. Advances in telephone communication both at home and to many overseas destinations like America, Canada and Australia came on in leaps and bounds, and then on 24th July 1936, the GPO introduced the speaking clock to the London area; the service received around thirteen million calls in its first year. It was extended to the rest of Britain in 1942. One of the main reasons why the GPO introduced this service was as an efficiency measure. Up until then, anyone wanting to know the right time would simply ring the operator and asked her what was the time by the clock on the exchange wall! Telephonist Jane Cain was the first voice of the speaking clock.

The following year, the 999 service was introduced in London and then to Glasgow in 1938. However, it was 1946 before the service was extended to other major towns and cities.

In Germany, the relentless grip on power of the Nazi Party was the cause of increasing concern as the thirties unfolded, particularly amongst the many Great War veterans who had experienced the horrors of that conflict. Its leader, Adolf Hitler, had been appointed as Chancellor by President Hindenburg on 30th January 1933. From that moment on, the die was cast. Hitler instructed Hermann Göring, the Great War air ace who had flown with Richthofen, to expand the state police. The Geheime Staatspolizei, the Gestapo, was the result.

Contrary to the Treaty of Versailles, Germany began to re-arm, and in 1936 Hitler sent his troops to reoccupy the Rhineland. In Britain, Stanley Baldwin did nothing. France did nothing. Unable and unwilling to contemplate the appalling prospect of another war in Europe, both governments followed a policy of appeasement towards the dictator. Emboldened, Hitler continued his re-armament programme and annexed Austria. By the summer of 1938, the situation in Europe had become critical. Hitler sought to invade the Sudetenland area of Czechoslovakia, attracted by its German-speaking population and mineral resources. However, he was not yet ready for war and wanted to know what Britain, now led by Neville Chamberlain, and France would do if he seized the area. France had only just completed much of its reconstruction work after the last war and could not afford another one.

Chamberlain wanted peace at almost any price. Baldwin had left us ill-equipped for war and Chamberlain had continued that policy. Twice in September he flew to Germany to meet with

Hitler. At the end of the month an agreement was reached in Munich; Hitler could have the Sudetenland and Europe would have peace. Chamberlain returned triumphant to Britain and announced at 10, Downing Street that he had brought 'peace in our time'.

Earlier in the month, Chamberlain had met Hitler at the Berghof, the dictator's private retreat at Berchtesgaden in Bavaria. At that meeting, a remarkable incident from the Great War came to light. Hanging upon the wall was a painting depicting a private soldier in the British Army carrying a wounded comrade to safety. When Chamberlain asked Hitler about the painting, the Chancellor took out his wallet, removed a newspaper cutting from it, which he slid across the table to Chamberlain, and then told the story. The painted scene was the Kruiseke crossroads, northwest of Ypres on 28th September 1918, and it depicted part of the action by Private Henry Tandy that led to the award of his Victoria Cross, having already been awarded the Distinguished Conduct Medal and the Military Medal.

The actions which had led to Tandy, who had already been Mentioned in Dispatches five times, being awarded his three gallantry medals all occurred between 28th August and 28th September 1918. Earlier that same day, at the French village of Marcoing, Private Tandy, serving with the 5th Duke of Wellington's Regiment, had seen a wounded German soldier wander into his line of fire. Tandy, a regular soldier who had sailed to France with the BEF in August 1914, was too close to miss his target but could not bring himself to shoot a wounded man and lowered his rifle. The German, resigned to his fate, had not even tried to raise his own rifle. He looked at the British soldier, nodded his appreciation at having had his life spared and continued on his way to have his wounds dressed.

Later, Tandy was severely wounded in the last moments of his VC action and was returned to Britain for treatment. With his three decorations all coming so closely together and including the VC, the press made much of Tandy's investiture, which came well after the Armistice. Newspapers were sent to the occupying troops in Germany. The now demobilised Adolf Hitler obtained a copy and recognised Henry Tandy's picture as the man who had spared his life at Marcoing. He cut the article from the newspaper and kept it in his wallet.

After the Berghof meeting, the story was relayed to Tandy, who, then working for the Triumph Motor Company in Coventry, confirmed that the incident had taken place at Marcoing, although twenty years later, he could not clearly remember the face of the soldier whose life he had spared that day in 1918. Then, it was just another German soldier who had for a few moments passed through his life; whether it had been Hitler or not, he could not say. If Hitler said that he was the soldier that Tandy had spared, then there was no reason to dispute it. However, within a year, the consequences of his kind act of humanity began to haunt him.

I was not there and so I cannot vouchsafe the veracity of this story. However, the account originated from Hitler not Tandy. I think it is inconceivable that in 1938, in the midst of a continental crisis which threatened another pan-European war, where the political and military stakes were so high, that Hitler should make up such a story. He was the Führer; millions of his people already adored him; this was a story giving another man the honour. We can never be totally sure about this story beyond the facts that the Kruiseke crossroads painting hung upon Hitler's wall at the Berghof; Chamberlain met him there; Hitler knew of Henry Tandy and he had the 1918 newspaper cutting of Tandy's actions and awards, which did not make reference to the incident; Tandy confirmed that he did indeed spare the life of a German soldier on 28th September 1918 at Marcoing, and Hitler was in the French village that day and had been wounded. Truth is so often stranger than fiction and such quite remarkable coincidences do occur in life and especially in war.

On Friday 1st September 1939, Germany invaded Poland. On Sunday, like everyone else in Britain that morning, Violet and I, together with Mary and Rowland, sat transfixed beside our wireless set listening to Neville Chamberlain announce that we were once more at war with Germany. My heart sank. The words brought back memories of the trenches, of the horrors, the sacrifices, and of Herbert. Surely we were not going to have to go through it all over again?

The weather was warm and sultry. Violet and I went for a walk in the afternoon which threatened a thunderstorm but it passed by. We knew that this time, Rowland would be the one to go. After this uncertain start, the month developed into one of the most beautiful Septembers I can recall. Dry and warm by day, although the nights were cold, and at the end of the month we had a sharp frost on the 28th. Each morning, low mist hung over the fields, the embodiment of John Keats' season of mists and mellow fruitfulness.

October carried the Indian summer forward. The bombers had not come, the gas attacks had not come and there was little to suggest that we were at war. We had our gas masks and had been promised an Anderson air-raid shelter for the garden. There were bombing attacks in Scotland and a submarine attack on the Royal Navy base at Scapa Flow, otherwise life went on as normal.

The winter of 1939–40 was bitterly cold with a lot of snow. The men of our Expeditionary Force had once again gone to France and were living in tents. I knew all about how miserable and debilitating such conditions were in bitterly cold weather and I felt very sorry for those young men.

On Tuesday 7th May, during the House of Commons debate upon the Norway debacle, Leo Amery wielded the knife at Chamberlain when he quoted Oliver Cromwell's words to the Long Parliament, *"You have sat too long here for any good you have been doing. Depart, I say, and let us have done with you. In the name of God, go."* On Friday 10th he did and Winston Churchill became Prime Minister.

The following Tuesday evening, Anthony Eden, now Secretary of State for War, called for volunteers to form a new Home defence force called the Local Volunteer Force, the LDV. Men above the age of conscription, those waiting for military service or in reserve occupations were eligible. Rowland and I both volunteered the next day at the police station. Eden had expected about 150,000 volunteers; by the end of June he had 1,500,000.

We were known as the Look, Duck and Vanish Brigade, because that's all we could do. We had no weapons. The Dunkirk evacuation had been able to rescue over 338,000 men from France, but they had left their weapons and equipment behind. Our main job at that time, when invasion was expected at any moment, was to report anything unusual or suspicious which we saw. The thinking behind it was that local people in each town or village were much more likely to notice anything out of place than would regular soldiers who were strangers to the area. In July, Churchill ordered the name to be changed to the Home Guard.

In time, the whole system was put on a more military footing and we were attached to the KSLI, the King's Shropshire Light Infantry; we were Wellington No.11 Sector. Rowland and I were both in A Company of the 5th Battalion, which had its HQ at the Drill Hall in King Street. One night Rowland was on duty there with the sergeant; just the two of them. They had one rifle and five rounds of ammunition between them to repel an attack by German paratroopers! During the night, they heard a terrible clatter outside. The sergeant told Rowland to go out and see what was going on and if it was an enemy paratrooper. Not unreasonably, my son asked if he could take the rifle and the ammunition.

"Not likely, lad," came the reply, "that's for me in case they come in 'ere." Sergeants!

In October 1940, Rowland turned eighteen and was eligible for military service. He was by now halfway through his apprenticeship and so his conscription was deferred until April 1943, at which point he was sent for and posted to Aldershot to start his military training. It was whilst in London one day that he first met his future wife, Hilda Rose Seager. By the time he was posted to Greece, they had become engaged. They married on 5th March 1947 and my daughter-in-law found herself with the initials HRH, much to her family's amusement. Their twins, Elaine and Martin were born in 1955. Mary met and married Leslie Chesters. They remained in Wellington and had two daughters, Jean and Christine.

I had continued working with the GPO all through the war, but, increasingly, my earlier wounds were troubling me. In August 1952 I turned sixty and could at last think about retiring. On 28th September at a formal presentation, I was awarded the Imperial Service Medal for thirty-eight years' service in war and peace. Just before the end of the year, I retired from the GPO. By then, I had lived in two centuries, on two continents, had seen the birth of the motor car and the aeroplane, served five monarchs and survived two world wars; it was time to retire.

With Violet on our wedding day. I was a lot slimmer after the war than the stocky farm boy who had gone to Canada!

'Roly up the pole'. Harley Bank in the 1920s. It's a far cry from the frenetic helter-skelter it is today.

Me, Violet, Hilda, Rowland, and Mary in 1947.

With the twins, Elaine, right, and Martin in 1955

Receiving my Imperial Service Medal –
28ᵗʰ September 1952.

My medals [l-r]: British War Medal, Victory Medal, Imperial Service Medal

CENTRAL CHANCERY OF
THE ORDERS OF KNIGHTHOOD
ST JAMES'S PALACE

26th. September, 1952.

Sir,

I am commanded to forward the Imperial Service Medal which Her Majesty The Queen has been graciously pleased to award to you in recognition of the meritorious services which you have rendered.

I have the honour to be, Sir,

Your obedient servant,

Ivan De la Bere

Brigadier
Registrar of the Imperial Service Order.

Rowland Hill, Esq.

My Imperial Service Medal citation

The Author

Born to Army officer parents at Gibraltar Military Hospital in 1949, Kenneth Ballantyne was educated at schools across Europe, Scotland and England. His father, a career soldier with the Royal Artillery, had served throughout the Second World War, as had his mother, who trained as a nurse at the outbreak of war and then joined the First Aid Nursing Yeomanry.

Part of Kenneth's early years were spent living and playing amongst the bomb craters left in the German Ruhr by RAF Bomber Command. At seven, his parents took him and his brother Iain to the Reichswald Forest War Cemetery to educate them both about the true price that had been paid for their lives and freedom, an experience which became an indelible memory for him.

After several years as a police officer, Kenneth graduated and then practised law as a solicitor before retiring to combine his love of writing with his interest in the personal experiences of those who fought in the World Wars, an interest which had grown out of that visit to the Reichswald Forest War Cemetery. A member of the Bomber Command Association, the Shropshire Aircrew Association, No.50/61 Squadrons Association and the Metheringham Airfield Museum, he now spends much of his time collecting and recording the true stories and experiences of the men and women who served on the Home Front and in the Armed Services during the war as an important historical project for an enduring legacy.

Kenneth established Laundry Cottage Books in 2005 in order to put his first book into print, and several other titles have followed. He has also helped veterans write their own accounts and Laundry Cottage Books has published some of these.

Kenneth gives lectures based around the books he writes to a wide variety of audiences across the country.